BEHAVIOUR THERAPY

BEHAVIOUR THERAPY

BEHAVIOUR THERAPY

PROCEEDINGS OF A SYMPOSIUM HELD BY THE
QUEENSLAND BRANCH OF THE AUSTRALIAN
PSYCHOLOGICAL SOCIETY, 1967

Edited by G. L. Mangan and
L. D. Bainbridge

UNIVERSITY OF QUEENSLAND PRESS

© University of Queensland Press, St. Lucia, Queensland, 1969

National Library of Australia registry number Aus 68-1228
Text is set in 11/11 Imprint
Printed and bound by Dai Nippon Printing Co. (International) Ltd., Hong Kong
Designed by Cyrelle

FOREWORD

This publication constitutes the major proceedings of a symposium on behaviour therapy organized by the Queensland branch of the Australian Psychological Society on 14 and 15 January 1967.

The seminars provided an opportunity for behaviour therapists to debate controversial issues, and for the audience to share in the interchange of ideas. By publishing the proceedings the branch hopes to make it possible for a wider audience to benefit. Editorial policy has been to make as few changes as possible to recorded proceedings. In a number of cases questions and discussion are reported verbatim. In this way, something of the personalities of the leading contributors might be revealed.

C. WILLIAMS

CHAIRMAN, QUEENSLAND BRANCH

AUSTRALIAN PSYCHOLOGICAL SOCIETY

BRISBANE

JULY 1967

PREFACE

In recent years new methods of behavioural modification, aimed at effecting socially useful changes in individual behaviour, have become available to psychotherapists. These techniques, which are classed under the generic term "Behaviour Therapy", have developed out of learning theory. Although based originally on experiments with animal subjects, they are now being applied to the modification of maladaptive behaviour in human beings. In contrast to classical interview therapies, it is claimed that they require less time and less skill on the part of the therapist, and effect a higher rate of success and lower relapse rate. If so, their attractiveness is obvious, and their general application a matter of highpriority.

It is possible that such claims are extravagant; this may reflect, however, the intransigence of some behaviour therapists rather than any inherent weakness in the methods themselves. A great amount of fundamental research must be done before the validity and general utility of many of these methods can be determined. While it is quite clear, for example, that monosymptomatic phobias, which have been relatively unresponsive to conventional treatment, are often amenable to modification using techniques such as systematic desensitization, it is equally apparent that many of the more complex disorders have been relatively unaltered by such methods. And while it is improbable that even "standard" treatments can be applied with efficacy to all subjects, it is equally unlikely that every subject is completely unique, demanding highly specific treatment. The study of behaviour indicates that there are general processes underlying behaviour, while at the same time individual differences in physiological and cultural environment impose both constraints and advantages in behavioural shaping and reshaping. These are issues for future research.

At the moment, behaviour therapy is at an unsophisticated theoretical level. In such a relatively new approach one would expect a divergence of opinion, particularly since many learning theory constructs are still extremely hypothetical. In addition, many of the classical problems — the continuity/discontinuity issue, for example — may assume a new significance in the light of this new approach. For some, the atheoretical approach of Skinner is the answer. Others attempt to blend the learning theories of Hull and Pavlov, Harlow and Atkinson, with, for example, recent theories concerning cognitive control of autonomic processes. Out of this may develop new or revised techniques which will utilize the high human potential for behavioural shaping conferred by a more complex nervous system and a second signal system of reality.

The participants in this symposium include academics involved in teaching and research in behaviour therapy, experimental psychologists, psychological and psychiatric practitioners, social workers, medical practitioners, and students, utilizing, or interested in utilizing, these techniques. All these interests and orientations are represented in the papers reported in the proceedings.

It is clear from these papers that many problems are only briefly touched upon in the seminars. That strong differences exist between many of the participants is obvious. That such differences are aired in this symposium is desirable. That confrontation of this sort will result in immediate rapprochement or radical reassessment is unlikely. Despite this, it is hoped that basic issues will be re-examined in the light of an expanded insight. And this ultimately is the purpose of such symposia.

We acknowledge permission granted by the journal *Behaviour Research and Therapy* to reproduce Figures 2 and 3 in N. McConaghy, "Aversion Therapy in the Treatment of Male Homosexuals".

G. L. MANGAN
L. D. BAINBRIDGE
UNIVERSITY OF QUEENSLAND
JUNE 1967

CONTENTS

SYMPOSIUM ORGANIZING COMMITTEE

C. Williams, B.A., B.Ed., M.A.Ps.S. (Chairman)
L. D. Bainbridge, B.A., B.Sc., M.A.Ps.S. (Honorary Secretary)
R. G. Farmer, B.A., M.A.Ps.S.
Elsie Harwood, M.A., Ph.D., A.B.Ps.S., M.A.Ps.S. (Convener)
G. L. Mangan, M.A., B.Ed., Ph.D., F.B.Ps.S., F.A.Ps.S.
B. Nurcombe, M.B., B.S., D.P.M., M.A.N.Z.C.P., M.A.Ps.S.
J. C. Winship, B.Ed., M.A., M.A.Ps.S.

SYMPOSIUM EDITORS

G. L. Mangan, M.A., B.Ed., Ph.D., F.B.Ps.S., F.A.Ps.S.
L. D. Bainbridge, B.A., B.Sc., M.A.Ps.S.

SYMPOSIUM CHAIRMEN

SEMINAR I
　　G. S. Urquhart, M.B., B.S., D.P.M., M.A.N.Z.C.P.
　　Director of State Psychiatric Services, Queensland

SEMINAR II
　　H. W. Thiele, M.A., Ph.D., M.A.Ps.S.
　　Director of Counselling Services, University of Queensland

SEMINAR III
　　A. J. Yates,[1] B.A., Ph.D., Dip.Psychol., F.A.Ps.S., F.B.Ps.S.
　　Professor of Psychology, University of New England, New
　　South Wales

SEMINAR IV
　　N. E. Parker, M.D., D.P.M., F.A.N.Z.C.P., M.A.Ps.S.
　　Psychiatrist, Brisbane, Queensland

CONTRIBUTORS

A. G. Hammer, M.A., M.A.Ps.S.
  Professor of Applied Psychology, University of New South Wales

Elsie Harwood, M.A., Ph.D., A.B.Ps.S., M.A.Ps.S.
  Senior Lecturer, Department of Psychology, University of Queensland

S. H. Lovibond, B.A., Ph.D., A.U.A., F.A.Ps.S., F.B.Ps.S.
  Reader, Department of Psychology, University of Adelaide

G. L. Mangan, M.A., B.Ed., Ph.D., F.B.Ps.S., F.A.Ps.S.
  Reader, Department of Psychology, University of Queensland

N. McConaghy, B.S., B.Sc., M.D., D.P.M.
  Senior Lecturer, School of Psychiatry, University of New South Wales

R. B. Milton, M.B., B.S.
  Medical Officer in charge of Alcoholism Clinics, Royal Brisbane Hospital and Wacol Rehabilitation Clinic, Brisbane, Queensland

B. Nurcombe,[2] M.B., B.S., D.P.M., M.A.N.Z.C.P., M.A.Ps.S.
  Child Guidance Clinic, Department of Health, Brisbane, Queensland

F. A. Whitlock, M.A., M.D., M.R.C.P., D.P.M.
  Professor of Psychological Medicine, University of Queensland

J. C. Winship, B.Ed., M.A., M.A.Ps.S.
  Psychiatric Clinic, Department of Health, Brisbane, Queensland

A J. Yates,[1] B.A., Ph.D., Dip.Psychol., F.A.Ps.S., F.B.Ps.S.
  Professor of Psychology, University of New England, New South Wales

1. Now at the University of Western Australia
2. Now at the University of New South Wales

BEHAVIOUR THERAPY:
AN ORIENTATION

Professor A. G. Hammer

In early times, the intra-individual difficulties of man were simply his difficulties, and were dealt with as effectively as possible by socially sanctioned helpers, the "medicine men". These difficulties may be loosely divided into those of body, mind, and (if you believe in its existence) soul. For example, there were problems of adapting to physical circumstances such as invading micro-organisms; problems of coping with meaningful situations, and especially interpersonal ones, such as loss of a loved person; and problems of one's relationship to God and the supernatural. The advance of modern "scientific" civilization has revolutionized the treatment of the physical maladaptations, now institutionalized through the profession of medicine. Affairs of the soul and the supernatural are dealt with by the clergy, the second derivative of primitive medicine man. Difficulties of the mind (or if you prefer it, of behaviour of the total organism), difficulties in adjustment to what the world and persons mean, have not however come to be catered for as yet finally and exclusively by any single distinct profession. The reasons for this need not concern us at present.

Of course, man did not have to grapple with his psychological problems unaided. Families came to the rescue. The law had its regulating and punitive aspects. Teachers devised ways and means of promoting learning and conformity, and social workers set out specifically to help families "make out" in the complex current society. Behavioural and mental difficulties often involve others, so that especially where the disorder was "acted out" in some sense, the existing traditional helpers, clergymen and doctors, were also called upon to give some aid in this area.

1

The early involvement of the clergy was by and large unfortunate. It was associated with theories of devil possession, witchcraft and the like, and treatment was therefore a matter of exorcism. However, the advances of biological science and of humanitarianism generally brought about some improvement in the lot of the mentally ill, and it may be that the more abiding residue of the activities of the men of God, namely the assumption that something more is required than ministration to a diseased body, was a good thing. This assumption, however, was for quite a time submerged, for it was the medical profession that took over the treatment of serious mental illness. Again we need not enquire into the reasons for this. The work of Pinel illustrates the trend. Furthermore it is certainly the case that much psychological disorder is a secondary consequence of primary physiological disease — as with syphylitic paresis, hyperthyroidism, etc. — and discoveries about these matters, and about ways of treating these diseases, were genuine first rate advances. Psychological disorder became a variety of illness and its treatment came to be looked upon, both by doctors and by others, as part of medicine. It has substantially remained so. Two of the outcomes are these: (a) There has been considerable hostile defensiveness on issues of professional demarcations, which seem to me interesting evidence of irrational "territoriality" in the species *Homo sapiens*. This, however, is not our direct concern at present. (b) What has been called the medical model came to exert a dominant influence in this area. One of the questions that has to be asked this weekend is whether this model is an appropriate one. But more on that in a moment.

Now, while some behaviour disorder is a consequence of bodily disease, it is now quite certain that some is not. This is not a contradiction of a materialist and determinist and even reductionist position — which position in fact I hold. Temper tantrums are more likely to be the outcome of a child's circumstances, of his psychological life-space, than of a tumour; sometimes even paralysis, blindness, hallucinations and serious mood pathology may arise from circumstances. The emphasis on this possibility was a part of Freud's contributions. Now if a patient's mental confusion is caused by toxins, it is irresponsible to try to cure it by repeated attempts to clarify the situation with verbal explanations. Freud clearly recognized *pari passu* that if a paralysis is caused by psychological factors, then it is these which have to be dealt with therapeutically. In practice, situations are of course not so clearly either one or the other as I am representing them for convenience of exposition. The behaviour therapists will not quarrel with this — but merely about the nature of the psychological factors and how they are to be dealt with.

The notion of psychogenesis was really a departure from the medical model, which indicates that the medical model is constituted of a number of notions and practices and does not have to be adhered to *in toto*. Therefore our task is not simply to decide whether the medical model is appropriate, but rather to analyse it into its parts and to determine the applicability of each part to the psychological treatment situation. In general the medical model seems an unlikely one to be suitable. People acquire patterns of responses to deal with situations. Changing them involves altering circumstances, correcting misunderstandings, learning new habits, changing one's goals, and so on. The appropriate model seems more like those of the remedial teacher, the politician, the salesman, the evangelist, the actor, or the parent — or does it? That is one basic question.

I suggest that some constituents of the medical model relevant to our present considerations are:

1. Diseases are diseases of the body. We have noted that Freud was ready to abandon this assumption.

2. Illness implies the intrusion into an otherwise normally functioning organism of disease-causing factors. Thus germs may invade the body. Freud did not abandon this. Complexes in the unconscious mind replace the germs. This assumption is not the assertion of an all-or-none variation — pneumonia may or may not be severe — but it does involve the idea of a qualitative difference as well, of some sort of discontinuity, or some going round the bend into a new dimension, the entrance into the scene of the villain of the piece.

3. The presence of the pathogenic factors is the real disease, not the particular symptoms which follow. Symptom-masking is not a real cure, since the presence of the pathogenic agent always threatens relapse.

4. The particular disease is determined by the particular pathogenic agent: diagnosis is a matter of discovering which agent, therapy a matter of counteracting it.

5. The counteraction is achieved either by (*a*) advice to the patient on what to do (rest, take drugs) or by (*b*) actually operating — away from life. It is interesting that Freud's operation was "free association"; and that in identifying the diagnostic procedure and therapy, and in treating almost all behaviour disorders as variants of the one pathogenic agent (viz. repressed conflicted wishes), he was also to an extent breaking away from the medical model.

6. The doctor diagnoses and treats in a socially accepted professional relationship, with status and privileges and responsibilities, but one that is relatively impersonal and non-involved.

My own opinion is that Freud (and the better of those who followed) accepted (2), (3), (5b), and (6), and that we need to know how sound and relevant these presumptions are.

Freud strove to treat the neuroses by counteracting their psychological causes. Probably Freud knew little of the formal discipline of psychology, and one may doubt whether he would have bothered to follow its development. But it is also fair to say that there existed no worth-while psychology for him to use. It was still coming into existence independent of philosophy, slowly developing laboratory techniques, and concerning itself with such matters as the analysis of experience into constituent images, or the determinants of depth perception, or of association reaction-time. I am confident that Professor Yates will want to argue — but I don't think he will need to preach this to many of us, who are the converted — that psychological treatment must be based on "academic" psychological science, just as electronics must be based on physics.

But the necessary psychology was simply not there for Freud to use. Nor had sufficient attention been given by psychologists to the possibility of specifically pathological mental processes. Even today I think academic psychology has too little to say about the causes and consequences of fears and hopes, loving and hating, disappointment, guilt, jealousy, boredom, surprises, and so on; and it is difficult, though some start has been made with work on pain, sensory deprivation, and voluntary starvation, to study whether behaviour changes qualitatively under conditions of extreme stress. For one thing, most laboratory subjects have the background assurance that the situation is not completely "dinkum". Further, things are not always what they seem — for example, capacity to tolerate a long time of sensory deprivation may not be indicative of some variable of ego strength, but of a pattern of motivations of the subject towards the experimenter. Had today's psychology been available to Freud, I doubt if he would have been much better off; and I and you must accept our share of responsibility for this! I am far from happy about the current state of general psychology.

Freud thus had to discover his own psychology. As you well know he came up with what he took to be the empirically based theory of conflict-originated repression of illicit wishes, disguised derivatives of which were slips, dreams, neurotic and psychotic symptoms, and pathological character traits. Treatment required

4

making the unconscious conscious. Free association was the basic technique. Subsequently it was (allegedly) discovered that the patient comes to relive in facsimile with the analyst the pathogenic interpersonal relationships with the important early figures of his life, and well-timed interpretations in the non-punitive atmosphere aid the patient's realizations of the true nature of the situation.

One relevant comment might be that this is a coherent, plausible and tenable view; perhaps it was well received after initial opposition because it was capable of making sense of what otherwise was chaotic. Of course there exists poor and indeed ridiculous analytic psychology, but it is our job at present to evaluate the best of behaviour therapy, which has its poor material, against the best dynamic psychiatry.

What have been the outcomes of this work? Everyone really knows that the outcome is broadly unsatisfactory. No doubt many factors have contributed to this — *inter alia*:

1. Psychogenesis, and psychoanalytically based therapy, have been broadly accepted by medicine. However, it would be economically impossible for psychiatrists to practise full-scale analysis. Thus a laughable but tragic consequence is that able young men study for six years at a university learning physics, chemistry, zoology, anatomy, physiology, pathology, clinical medicine, neurology, and so on, and some years in hospital learning to prescribe drugs and perform surgery, and then, thus trained, go to work helping people who are in difficulties because of, say, their love life, which the doctors have never seriously studied at all, by general psychological techniques such as interviewing, reassuring, suggestion, and group discussion which they have never practised at all and which are in fact of dubious efficacy.

2. The results achieved by full-scale, fully trained psychoanalysts have been unsatisfactory. Individual case studies are impressive — the logic is that of the jig-saw puzzle — but over-all results are not distinguishably better than non-specialist treatment. Obviously something is wrong somewhere, and maybe the whole account is wrong. However, the situation needs to be looked at quite closely.

The following are some relevant points:

(*a*) The theory may be right, but of difficult application.

(*b*) Part of the theory may be right and part wrong. In particular, the account of how recovery comes about is particularly weak. Freud may give a descriptive account of aetiology, but no sufficient explanation of maintenance to indicate treatment. He himself became therapeutically pessimistic; and if the theory predicts non-recovery, which occurs, the theory is supported!

(*c*) The theory may apply to some sorts of cases and not to others.

5

Unfortunately psychoanalysis tended to become a "general psychology" instead of concentrating on pathology. I am not urging a return to the view that the mentally ill should be viewed as pariahs. We all have illnesses. But it is still possible to view illness as something apart. Psychoanalysis moved to treatment of minor personality maladjustments (e.g. inferiority feelings) and even everyday adjustments (e.g. marital adjustment). It seems to me most unsatisfactory that different disorders have not been taken up separately. It may be that stammering, enuresis, and over-frequent temper tantrums have nothing to do with repressed complexes, and need to be dealt with in ways other than analytic.

This leads one to ask — assuming that "behaviour therapy" is a narrower term than just "treatment" — to what disorders is behaviour therapy deemed applicable? It is my personal opinion that the dynamic theories and therapies were originally developed to cope with persistent unrewarding irrational behaviour — the neurotic paradox such as unwanted aphonia or paralysing compulsive rituals. Such symptoms came to the attention of healers rather than parents precisely because they seemed immune to ordinary re-educative techniques. Whether they are really immune to re-educative techniques is another issue. Parents often think of repeated arguments and explanation as re-educating, whilst psychologists of all persuasions would be critical of such appeals to rationality. It may be that re-educative techniques have until recently not been tried. Guthrie perhaps merits most praise for underlining this.

3. Some changes occurred in psychoanalytic type theory too: (a) Some of these changes seemed to assume that the theory was working along the right lines, but had to sort out the details — hence material on Oedipus complexes, castration anxieties, and so on. (b) I think it fair to say that psychoanalysis does not have in the movement sufficient of the scientific method to locate the issues to be tested and to devise thorough tests, to do a root and branch job. Yet even here its willingness to grapple with the content of the themes of living seems to me a feature not to be completely ignored. (c) Other changes seem to be more in the direction of common sense, and I think them none the better for that reason. For example there has been a tendency to emphasize general motives rather than specific repressed memories, the current situation rather than the residues of the past, social rather than biological factors. There has been no reason to think results improved. A common defence of the situation is that basic personality is improved, even though symptoms are unchanged. The same claim might be made by Sunday School teachers, but this

6

would seem to remove the discussion from the proper area of treating behaviour disorders.

4. Psychoanalysis has influenced psychology, but because of its medical affiliations, its initial defensiveness against hostility, and its early independence of psychological science, it has remained relatively uninfluenced by academic psychology, and indeed, prone to exclude psychologists. The short supply of psychological helpers, the failures of dynamic psychiatry, and the exclusion of psychologists from a sensible role have led to other treatment movements sponsored by psychologists. There are, I suggest, two worthy of consideration – (*a*) non-directive psychotherapy and (*b*) behaviour therapy. These are currently with us, perhaps still fighting for a place in the sun! That seems to me the contextual background for this conference.

NON-DIRECTIVE PSYCHOTHERAPY

I must be brief in commenting on non-directive therapy simply because it is not our present topic. In the light of what I have said about dynamic psychiatry, I shall merely make the following assertions.

1. Although it is a psychologist's movement, non-directive therapy is quite like dynamic psychiatry — permissive interviewing, conflicting emotions.

2. The psychologists are aware of general psychology, but still develop most of their theory out of therapy session data (theory in terms of self, anxiety, and self awareness, locus of evaluation).

3. This group has made adequate use of the scientific method in the study of the results achieved and in the internal study of the individual case. However, it is probably the case that control subjects have been too exclusively the untreated rather than the otherwise treated.

4. The results are fair. However, again one witnesses the improvement of capacity to tolerate symptoms rather than their disappearance — which could come from, say, conversion to Christianity.

5. Although a professional and consulting relationship is retained, emphasis is on a genuine (real-life) personal relationship. The technician part of the medical model has gone.

BEHAVIOUR THERAPY

It is possible that Professor Yates may disagree with my use of this term to refer to what follows. He may prefer to specify more narrowly than I what is included in it, and also to include some procedures which I would not. Frankly I do not know the history of the phrase, and, so long as communication is not hampered, I don't think it matters very much whether X means A and Y means B, or vice versa. Thus I am quite willing to abandon the term behaviour therapy but not the opinion that what follows involves a real issue to be thrashed out.

Whilst the psychoanalysts were making their own psychology, changes were occurring in academic psychology. In particular, Watson initiated the behaviourist movement, utilizing Pavlov's conditioned reflex as the basic unit, and developing a psychology that was (a) objective, (b) functionalist, and (c) associative. There were fortunately other functionalist movements, which were not associative and not so completely objective, notably the purposivist and Gestalt schools. I wish to draw attention to the "associative" feature which has remained characteristic of behaviourism, i.e. as a sort of version of domino theory, it proposes a succession of S ——→ R events, where Rs themselves operate as parts of the ensuing Ss — although there are different versions of what strengthens the bonds between an S and an R.

It was not long before the work on conditioning of emotional responses was reported, although I am not quite sure that the story of Little Albert and the White Rabbit hasn't some of the properties of a fairy-tale, and subsequently the work on reconditioning or counter-conditioning. Despite its uncomplicated character, this perhaps is a model of the sort of treatment which is being weighed against dynamic analytic therapy. I would ask you to observe that when it was reported, this work was judged to be at the heart of ordinary attitude learning and personality re-education, but not to have any special bearing on psychopathology or psychotherapy. In my opinion, it was assumed that the fear of white furry objects was not the prototype of the irrational intractable and consciousness-and-behaviour-dominating phobia. Thus from the behaviourist end too we come to the question which I think behaviour therapists must answer— to what phenomena are the doctrines of behaviouristic treatments deemed applicable? In particular, is it held that neurotic symptoms such as compulsions, obsessions and hysterical conversions are also instances of "normal" (in respect of process) conditioned responses to be dealt with by whatever processes undo such a reflex?

The objectivist behaviourist psychologists did not apparently think of their early work as a basic contribution to psychopathology, but did go on to apply their objective approach to the area. Thus Pavlov and his co-workers came, partly by accident, to study behaviour disorders in the dog. However, it will be noted that they argued for distinctively pathogenic events — particularly severe conflictual arrangements of stimulus situations — and rationalized this in terms of a theory of relationships between excitatory and inhibitory "tendencies" within the cerebral cortex. Masserman took the same line, and extended the work to try to show, with animal experimentation, how the stresses of conflict might be alleviated. In a way he was really trying to show that this line of study and that of the psychoanalysts were convergent. Miller and Dollard did little more than try to show that Freudianism could be translated into behaviourist terminology, but again they tended to lose sight of the possibility that there is something qualitatively different in pathogenic processes, tending to take the view that all acquisitions, neurotic or otherwise, are instances of the one and the same learning process, and some of them merely happen to be pathological because of the "content" of what has been learnt. They do seem to allow that there is some special danger in learning not to think of a "topic" — i.e. in repression, and in the mediation of the anxiety response.

One investigator in the same broad tradition who took a somewhat independent line was Maier. He supported the view that under conditions of frustration (a situation where an insoluble problem must be solved) organisms cease to show adaptive behaviour, and instead exhibit non-adaptive fixations. He thus avoids the Freudian solution of looking for covert pseudo-adaptations. Critics are dubious about the notion of completely non-adaptive behaviour, and suggest that Maier's rats may be showing, from their point of view, adaptive avoidance responses. However, he is able to show certain other features in the results which support his position.

The notion of breakdown to "behaviour without a goal" is intriguing, plausible, and accepts the discontinuity principle. Maier importantly goes on to show that erroneous learning has to be dealt with by the ordinary procedures of experimental extinction, discrimination learning, etc., but that these procedures are not of value with fixations. Fixations may be dealt with by guidance, a kind of passive learning, which, when it works, works almost instantaneously, as though all the learning has been done but something has to be broken through to permit its use. I think it doubtful whether Maier's work has been sufficiently applied to *Homo sapiens*. The guidance programme implies a getting out into life and living with the patient which no doubt is quite difficult to make compatible with the professional role. Even within the ranks of the Pavlovian oriented experimentalists there is disagreement about interpretations. Thus Liddell, working with sheep, and observing phenomena similar to the neuroses of Pavlov's dogs and Masserman's cats, has argued that the mechanistic interpretation is insufficient, and that understanding of what is going on requires that the context be taken into account. The context here consists essentially of what we may call the pattern of interpersonal relationships of the animal.

However, over the last decade or so, and I presume partly because of the therapeutic failure of dynamic psychiatry, there has emerged the definite trend to apply the "principles of unlearning of conditioned responses" in piecemeal and engineering fashion to the various symptoms of behaviour disorder. Knight Dunlap had given an early hint of this without being a reflexologist or behaviourist when he came out with his notion that repetition is the antithesis of learning and that unlearning is best achieved by negative practice — now, by "conditioning reactive inhibition". At first he applied this to motor habits (e.g. typewriting errors, stammering), but tried to extend it to neuroses in general. Neurosis he identified with over-introspection, and free association worked because it was massed practice of introspection! However, Dunlap did not really take on. It was rather for Wolpe, the Maudsley group, and a variety of American workers including the Skinnerians, to shape the existing trends into the current movement or vogue for the treatment of behaviour disorders by direct application of the principles of unlearning conditioned responses. It is not for me to go into details of this, but it has been implicit in the previous account that I think some distinguishing features (ones which must be examined) of the position are:

1. The approach must be scientific, and more narrowly objective.

2. There are no uniquely pathogenic situations and processes — all acquisition is learning, all treatment relearning. I would argue that not all acquisitions arising from experience need be of the one sort. One may acquire conditioned reflexes, also understanding, boredom, intentions, etc. — and by different processes. Possibly repressed dissociated complexes may be acquired.

3. A sufficient psychology in general is a psychology which gives an account of the reinforcement and weakening of associative bonds.

4. This psychology enables a seriatim attack on the symptoms rather than a consideration of and participation in a total thematic life pattern. But although somewhat impersonal it is not necessarily so, and it implies that possibility of going beyond consultation, and it certainly gets away from the emphasis on words.

A final comment. I am very inexpert on behaviouristic or learning theory type of psychology. One cannot keep up with everything, and long ago I inclined to the view that the associative, mechanistic CR position in general psychology was not correct — that McDougall, Tolman and Lewin were more likely to be more nearly correct than Pavlov, Watson, Hull and Spence. Even in physics there is recognition that things in action have effects different from things at rest, and that even things apparently at rest may be pressing for action in a specifiable direction — think, for example, of a drawn bow-and-arrow system.

In particular, the concept of an intention (Zeigarnik) seems to me a central one for psychologists, one that has not been developed, but which I think non-reducible to a CR. I look to Harlow, to Atkinson and Hilgard rather than to Hull, Skinner and Spence. Work on post-hypnotic suggestion hints at the possibility of persistent dynamic intentions, persisting possibly because of their cut-offness. Such dissociated intentions could conceivably be the basis of psychopathology. It is not the place here to develop this line, but I want to put it up as a viable alternative to the behaviour therapy line, an alternative which has not been thoroughly tried out although the relative failure of dynamic psychiatry is rather against it. On the other hand it still remains to be shown that behaviour therapy is effective if all the suggestion effects and interpersonal motivational effects are removed.

In Sydney University it is probably fair to say that for years Professor Champion has stood for a behaviouristic psychology and I for a modified purposivism. He taught general psychology, I taught psychopathology. One misgiving assails me. I doubt whether the movements of a primitive organism — say a shell fish — owe anything to either cognitions or intentions. Cognitions and intentions seem to be emergent possibilities requiring great neural complexity and organization. On the other hand even I know that under laboratory conditions — and without too much influence from the cognized context — humans do acquire CRs. Perhaps the primitive exists along with the evolved complex beside it. Is there the possibility that pathology occurs when primitive CRs take over from cognition and intention, that behaviour therapists have the right ways of treating the irrational, and that either Champion should have taught psychopathology and I general psychology, or both of us should have changed our systematic adherences?

However that be, it is my firm belief that the present seminar is still basically concerned with the issue that separated Watson and McDougall, and that the current conflict of views is merely another instance of the basic division amongst psychologists between elementarist, mechanistic, associationist thinkers, and those who think it necessary to use concepts implying recognition of field forces or purposing. Really I want Professor Yates, Dr. Lovibond and others to sort that one out for me — which is quite a tall order.

REFERENCES

1. In this paper, general references are not cited. These can be located in Boring, E.G. (1950), *A history of experimental psychology*, 2nd ed. New York: Appleton-Century-Crofts, and in Murphy, G. (1949), *Historical introduction to modern psychology*. New York: Harcourt, Brace and World.

SEMINAR ONE : A CRITICAL SURVEY
OF THE THEORY AND PRACTICE
OF BEHAVIOUR THERAPY

SEMINAR ONE : PAPER ONE

Professor A. J. Yates

As each of the speakers in this particular part of the symposium is allowed only twenty minutes, and as I do not wish to exceed that time so that there will be as much time as possible left afterwards for discussion, I am going to confine myself to a relatively small number of points, and then comment at the end on some of the things Professor Hammer said.

First of all, on the nature of behaviour therapy, I think it is important to state at this point that it is a little misleading to talk about behaviour therapy as if it were a single thing. In fact the term "behaviour therapy" can subsume a number of rather different and divergent approaches, all of which have some things in common, as Professor Hammer pointed out, but between which are also equally important differences which we should recognize. I want to indicate at this stage a quite distinct and definite bias on my own part as to what behaviour therapy really is. So I will describe what I conceive to be the three major approaches within the general field of behaviour therapy, then state what I think are the main differences between these three approaches, and then give you a definition of behaviour therapy as I see it at present. As Professor Hammer pointed out, my definition of behaviour therapy is a personal one; but it is one which, I think, is important, and does differ from the approaches of some of the other workers in this field.

There are three major approaches which derive from South Africa, the United Kingdom and America. Those of you who have read the critical article by Breger and McGaugh[1] published in the *Psychological Bulletin* will know that they classify, or attempt to classify, certain schools of behaviour therapy, and in my paper to the Australian Psychological Society last year I tried to indicate how I thought that Breger and McGaugh were in very serious error in the kinds of classification they used. This was largely the result of failure to appreciate or even to know about the historical development of behaviour therapy. Now I do not propose to recapitulate the whole of that talk, but rather to select out some of the more important points in it which a good many of you may not have heard. For those of you who have heard what I have said before, I must apologize, but I think it is important to get these differences straight.

One strand, which developed in the 1950's, was the South African strand of Wolpe and Lazarus. These workers are largely responsible for what, in my view, is a quite incorrect notion, that behaviour therapy is the application of learning theory to the understanding and treatment of behavioural disorders. They regard abnormalities of behaviour primarily as failure to learn, on the one hand, or as faulty or inappropriate learning on the other. Consequently their methods of treatment largely employ learning theory constructs, and methods derived from those constructs. The most famous of these methods, of course, is reciprocal inhibition therapy.

During the same period, in the United States, a quite different approach to the objective study of abnormalities of behaviour was being developed by Ogden Lindsley, who based his ideas on the methods of Skinner, and the so-called atheoretical approach of the operant conditioners. This approach has been, as it were, vieing with the Wolpe-Lazarus approach, although both Wolpe and Lazarus are now in the United States and, as far as I know, both at Philadelphia. The Skinner and Lindsley approach has led to a whole string of important research by people like Krasner, Ullmann, Goldiamond, Ferster, and so on, in a very wide variety of fields. They are, of course, learning "people", but one hesitates to call them learning "theorists", because Skinner denies that theories of learning are necessary.

Historically, it is interesting to note that Lazarus was incorrect, as far as I can gather, in claiming that he was the first person to use the term "behaviour therapy", as he has done in a recent book on his techniques. As far as I can discover, the first person to use the term "behaviour therapy" in a meaningful sense within this context was Ogden Lindsley, in 1954.

The third approach, which can be subsumed under the heading "behaviour therapy", was developed at the Maudsley in the early 1950's from the ideas of a person who is now seldom mentioned in discussions on behaviour therapy, but who in my opinion was its father, and that is M. B. Shapiro, who was and is head of the clinical teaching section at the Maudsley hospital. The approach at the Maudsley developed out of a general dissatisfaction with the role of the clinical psychologist at that time. As far as I can discover, the role of the clinical psychologist, particularly in the U.S.A., has not in fact changed very much since. We were dissatisfied at the Maudsley with being simply offsiders to the psychiatrist, the psychiatrist sending us patients and asking us psychiatric-type questions which were largely meaningless to us. We attempted to answer these questions largely by the use of the approach of battery testing.

Shapiro's feeling was that the basic role of the clinical psychologist vis-à-vis psychiatry should be essentially that of fundamental research worker, by analogy with the kind of fundamental research which goes on in the fields of general medicine. Within the field of psychiatry, there has not been such a tradition of fundamental research work, except on the biochemical and genetic side. Leaving aside those disorders which are clearly diseases analogous to medical diseases, if abnormalities of behaviour are largely acquired abnormalities or failure to acquire the particular forms of behaviour — notice clearly that I am not necessarily talking about "learning" now — and if behaviour in general is determined by laws which psychologists discover, then it should follow, in my opinion, that the proper role of the clinical psychologist who has spent many years in training in that body of knowledge and techniques which we call psychology should be that of fundamental research. By research here I mean research both into the causes of disorders and into changing these disorders.

The particular contribution of Shapiro[2] was to argue that it is possible to apply laboratory techniques, which are so familiar in the field of experimental psychology, not only in the abnormal field, but — and this is his major contribution to the study of the individual patient — to treat the individual patient as an object of experimentation under controlled conditions. From this it was a very short step to argue that if we could attempt to discover what was wrong with the patient, why he came into hospital, why it was he was unable to adjust to the outside world, then we should likewise be able to apply similar control techniques to change behaviour. As I pointed out in my Australian Psychological Society talk, this is, in my view, fundamentally what behaviour therapy is about. Therefore I would define behaviour therapy as the attempt to utilize, systematically, that body of empirical and theoretical knowledge which has resulted from the application

17

of experimental methods of psychology and the closely related disciplines of physiology and neurophysiology, in order to explain the genesis and maintenance of abnormal patterns of behaviour, and to apply that knowledge to the treatment or prevention of those abnormalities, by means of controlled experimental studies.

I think that this definition is critical because there is a very grave danger at the present time that behaviour therapy will become institutionalized, that is, it will be regarded as a standard set of techniques to be applied in particular instances. And there is no doubt, as my recent visit to America showed, that this is beginning to happen in the United States. The critical point about the definition I have just given is that it says nothing whatsoever about any theory. It is interesting to note in fact that Eysenck[3] himself in a recent definition of behaviour therapy has described it as the application of learning theory. In my view it is not, and never has been, specifically the application of any theory whatsoever. It is an attempt to examine, under controlled conditions, the behaviour of a patient, and to modify that behaviour along certain lines.

What is tending to happen in the U.S.A. is that people are beginning to say, for example, "Here is a patient who has a phobia. The preferred method of treatment in behaviour therapy of patients with phobias is systematic desensitization therapy. Wolpe tells us how we carry out systematic desensitization therapy. It involves teaching a patient to relax, with or without the use of hypnosis, it involves drawing up hierarchies of fear, and then it involves the application of a particular technique." The main point I wish to raise here is that, in my view, this is not what behaviour therapy is at all, because in behaviour therapy there are no standard techniques. Each patient presents a new problem.

I do not wish to imply that we will never have standard techniques. In fact, I will revoke that statement at once and say that one of the few areas where a standard method of treatment appears to have been developed is that of enuresis, about which Dr. Lovibond will have something to say. But on the whole, I think that we simply have to accept that human behaviour is so complex, and we know so little about the laws governing it, that to suppose that within the next twenty or fifty years we will have standard methods of treatment of behavioural abnormalities is simply hopelessly wishful thinking.

One difficulty in abnormal psychology, in my view, has been the tendency to reiterate, over and over again, that the patient's interests are the prime consideration. I am going to state bluntly that I do not believe that this is so, not in the short term. I believe

18

that we have to think also of the patients in the future — patients of twenty years hence — and I believe that we have to compromise, with those of us who are most skilled at making use of such knowledge as we have doing what we can for the patient, while those who are specially skilled in research have to be given the opportunities and the money to do the research. No one criticizes, at this stage, the worker in the field of cancer who carries out laboratory experiments on rats; on the effects, for instance, of cigarette smoke on the formation of cancerous tissues in rats. No one argues that he should really be treating a patient with cancer. And yet in the field of psychiatry, in particular, there has been a reluctance to accept the idea of a basic research worker, who may be making no contribution whatsoever to the amelioration of the behavioural pathology of particular individual patients.

One further point — I do not want to trespass on what Dr. Lovibond is going to say — but a further example of the institutionalization of behaviour therapy has arisen in recent studies comparing behaviour therapy with normal psychotherapy of various kinds, or with no treatment at all. In my view, most of this work is largely a complete waste of time; it follows directly from my definition of behaviour therapy that these kinds of studies are not critical in testing the efficacy of behaviour therapy. The efficacy of behaviour therapy can only be tested at the present time on an internal basis, that is, the control is the experimental manipulation of the individual patient. The comparison of large groups of patients involves the assumption, as you see if you read those papers, that there are standardized methods of treatment which we call behaviour therapy. Thus in the Marks and Gelder study,[4] we have a group of patients with phobias who are treated by what is called systematic desensitization therapy. Now the whole point that I am making is that there is not, and certainly should not be, in terms of my definition, any standard methods of systematic desensitization therapy, because systematic desensitization therapy is a variable which needs experimental investigation itself. It can be stated quite unequivocally that at present we know virtually nothing about systematic desensitization therapy.

Finally, let me point to the difference between behaviour therapy as it was developed at the Maudsley, and behaviour therapy as it was developed by the operant conditioners. The definition that I have given is virtually identical with the definition which has been given of the kinds of procedures which the operant conditioners utilize. The main difference between the Skinnerians, as I might call them, and the English behaviour therapists is simply that the English behaviour therapists are much more ready to make use of intervening variables, or constructs. This is relevant to what Professor Hammer said. I do not know what he means by an "intention", but I do wish to stress that the English behaviour therapists at least, and certainly the Wolpeans (Wolpe and his co-workers), have no objections whatsoever to the use of constructs. They are not peripheralists; they merely appear to be rather simple-minded because they prefer to start with what appear to be (and undoubtedly are not) relatively simple disorders — tics, stuttering, and so on. These disorders are not simple but at least you can measure the behaviour of the patient.

However, as you will see when I give my second talk, the English behaviour therapists in particular have made considerable use of intervening constructs. I know that constructs such as habit strength are certainly not what Professor Hammer means by intention. If Professor Hammer can tell me what "intentions" are, then I shall be quite happy to use them. If he can give me some kind of operational definition, so that I can get some kind of measurement, then I shall be quite happy to use any constructs he likes to name. I do not think there should be any limitations at all on the kinds of theoretical notions that one should use. The crucial thing is whether one can manipulate what the patient does or says or thinks or any other kind of response, either directly or indirectly observable, or whether it is a pure construct which cannot directly be measured.

REFERENCES

1. Breger, L. & McGaugh, J.L. (1965). Critique and reformulation of "learning-theory" approaches to psychotherapy and neurosis. *Psychol. Bull.* **63**, 338-58.
2. Shapiro, M.B. (1966). The single case in clinical psychological research. *J. gen. Psychol.* **74**, 3-23.
3. Eysenck, H.J., *ed.* (1964). *Experiments in behaviour therapy.* Oxford: Pergamon.
4. Marks, I.M. & Gelder, M.G. (1965). A controlled retrospective study of behaviour therapy in phobic patients. *Br. J. Psychiat.* **111**, 561-73.

SEMINAR ONE : **PAPER TWO**

Dr. S. H. Lovibond

In the time available to me I propose to consider, firstly, the question of the efficacy of behaviour therapy, and, secondly, the major criticisms of the behaviour therapist's approach. In view of Professor Yates's contribution, I feel I must begin by making clear the sense in which I propose to use the term behaviour therapy. When I speak of behaviour therapy, I will be referring to a set of relatively standardized procedures. It seems to me that this is what most people have in mind when they talk about behaviour therapy at present. While I have a good deal of sympathy for Professor Yates's point of view, I would not want to make such a sharp distinction as he does between the application of general principles and the application of the experimental method to the individual case. Clearly, then, I will be talking about behaviour therapy in a more conventional sense than Professor Yates.

It seems to me that despite the limitations of much of the behaviour therapy literature, it is now possible to reach a number of general conclusions about the effectiveness of behaviour therapy procedures. For our present purpose it is useful to think of behaviour disorders as lying along a continuum of severity and complexity. At one end of such a continuum would be the relatively "simple", monosymptomatic behaviour disorders, with enuresis defining the end point. Some of the more limited sorts of phobias would occupy an intermediate position, and right at the other end would be disorders which are chronic, complex, highly generalized, and incapacitating. These disorders, by anybody's definition, would be described as neuroses.

21

In the case of disorders of the monosymptomatic variety, it is not overwhelmingly difficult, in my view, to select groups which are equivalent for the purposes of experimental comparison, to determine the rate of spontaneous recovery and to establish criteria of successful treatment. Here I disagree rather strongly with Professor Yates's view that most of the experimental comparisons of different forms of therapy so far conducted have been a waste of time.

The evidence for the efficacy of behaviour therapy in relation to the simpler types of disorder, is, I believe, quite clear cut. Behaviour therapy is highly, even dramatically, effective. Taking enuresis as an example, the rate of initial arrest — or initial elimination of the symptom if you like to think of it that way — is around 90-95 per cent when the treatment is carried out properly.[1] Murray Coote in Melbourne has now treated over a thousand cases by standardized conditioning procedures, and has achieved an arrest rate of something like 90 per cent. Recent work that Coote and I[2] have carried out suggests that cases with diurnal urgency and frequency are often difficult to deal with, but new techniques are promising to overcome some of the problems.

In the case of the simpler phobias, there is again evidence that an initial elimination rate of something like 90 per cent can be achieved.[3,4,5] As we move towards more complex disorders, however, the evidence becomes less clear cut, and the suggestion is that the rate of success decreases rather substantially. Recently some very favourable results have been achieved in the treatment of homosexuality by aversion therapy,[6] but the overall picture is rather obscure, and I feel that a large comparative study will be necessary to establish firm conclusions in this area. The evidence is now mounting that severely and chronically disturbed patients do not respond as well to behaviour therapy as do less severely disturbed patients. This is a finding of Cooper and his associates,[4,5] and of a study that is being conducted at the Maudsley but which is not yet completed.

Despite the promise of operant procedures in the treatment of such children's disturbances as autism,[7] I think it is wiser at the present stage to reserve judgment on the effectiveness of these methods.

At present, relapse seems to be a problem of some magnitude in many areas of behaviour therapy. In the case of enuresis, the present relapse rate is about 30 per cent, and a high relapse rate has also been observed in alcoholics and homosexuals treated by behaviour therapy. It is now clear also that a proportion of successfully treated phobics subsequently relapse.[3,4] Nevertheless, the general principles of behavioural control derived from laboratory studies suggest ways in which the permanency of learning in behaviour therapy can be increased. Consequently, I feel we have every reason to expect substantial progress with the problem of relapse in the near future.

Let me summarize here by saying that the usefulness of behaviour therapy in some areas of treatment is now beyond question. Its effectiveness cannot be approached by any other form of treatment in the case of circumscribed disturbances which are under direct stimulus control. The value of behaviour therapy in the treatment of more severe disorders is not as well established, but the range of effective application of the techniques has yet to be determined. Relapse remains a problem to be dealt with, but the indications are that solutions will be forthcoming. Finally, it should be borne in mind that new techniques are constantly being devised, and old ones are being improved. Furthermore, the recent emphasis on experimental analysis of treatment procedures is bound to lead to further advances.

Now let me move on to consider criticisms which have been made of the behaviour therapy approach, ranging from the trivial to the serious. Frequently offered criticisms include the following:

1. Behaviour therapy is an inhuman, mechanical, pugilistic set of procedures for manipulating people.

2. No substantial improvement in neurotic conditions is possible without directing attention to the underlying causes of the illness.

3. Any beneficial results achieved by behaviour therapists are due to non-specific suggestion, or to transference effects.

4. Direct elimination of symptoms will result in symptom substitution or exacerbation of anxiety.

5. Behaviour therapy is useful only in the treatment of monosymptomatic disorders.

6. Behaviour therapy is unsound, because its theoretical basis is superficial or invalid.

Let me take these criticisms in turn. Firstly, in connection with the criticism that behaviour therapy procedures are inhuman and mechanical, I think it is necessary to point out that ordinary considerations of acceptance of the patient, and respect for him as a person, apply just as much in behaviour therapy as in any other form of therapy. In most cases the patient is given a description of the therapeutic goal, and the procedures to be used, in terms that are meaningful to him, and his responsibility as an intelligent participant is stressed. If the methods to be used are aversive, the patient is given a realistic appreciation of the chances of success on which to base his decision whether or not to accept treatment. The first criticism then is invalid.

The contention that insight into the causes of neurotic conditions is necessary to effect substantial improvement can also be dealt with summarily. The demonstrable effectiveness of such procedures as desensitization, despite lack of attention to etiological conditions, answers this criticism quite effectively.

Thirdly, the suggestion that any beneficial effects of behaviour therapy are the results of suggestion or transference is contradicted by all sorts of considerations arising out of the course of therapeutic change, i.e. the actual changes that can be observed in the course of therapy. For example, it has been a general finding in the treatment of multiple phobias that only the phobia under direct treatment manifests change, and those not being directly treated remain intact.[5] Exactly the same thing has been observed in the treatment of enuresis. It is possible to remove the enuretic symptom, leaving a complex of other symptoms totally unchanged. More than this, there is now direct experimental evidence that in the area of desensitization, the specific procedures are necessary for therapeutic success. Working with snake and spider phobic subjects, Lang and his associates[8] and Rachman[9] have shown that personal relationships plus relaxation are ineffective, and specific desensitization procedures are necessary for improvement to occur. Finally, evidence against the suggestion - transference notion comes from the experimental studies that have shown behaviour therapy to be considerably more effective than psychotherapy in the treatment of enuresis.[2]

Despite the very close attention that has been paid to the problem of symptom substitution, very few examples have been reported in the literature. The fact that there have been so few reports of symptom substitution seems to me to attest to the honesty of many of the psychodynamically oriented people. The idea that direct elimination of symptoms must always lead to symptom substitution is thus demonstrably unsound. Furthermore, when effects on general psychological adjustment have followed the successful removal of symptoms, those effects have almost invariably been beneficial rather than harmful.

The fifth criticism, that behaviour therapy is useful only in monosymptomatic cases, obviously is not true. Apart from the fact that multiple phobias can be tackled successfully, there is recent evidence that rather highly generalized anxiety symptoms can be alleviated by appropriate procedures.[10] Nevertheless, I would agree that it does seem to be the case that the further we move towards the non-specific, highly generalized forms of disorder, such as pervasive anxiety or depression, the less are our chances of success. That seems to be the picture at the moment, but of course it is subject to change in the light of further developments. Parenthetically we might add that there is no evidence that other forms of psychological treatment are particularly effective in the case of the more complex and generalized disorders.

This brings us to the final criticism — that the theoretical basis of behaviour therapy is inadequate. This, I feel, is the only criticism of behaviour therapy that has any validity and as such it deserves serious consideration. In taking up the question of the adequacy of behaviour therapy theory, the first point I wish to make is that, to a very large degree, behaviour therapy is the application of a technology of behavioural control rather than the application of a theory of the nature of behaviour disorders. That is to say, in the main behaviour therapy is the clinical application of principles of behavioural control which have been developed through laboratory study of normal animal behaviour. For example, in aversion therapy we make use of the principle that a response will be suppressed if it is closely and consistently followed by strong aversive reinforcement. What constitutes aversive reinforcement is of course an empirical matter. I would contend that the great majority of behaviour therapy techniques were developed by the "let's try it and see" method, rather than being derived explicitly from theory. For example, the development of the Mowrer technique for treating enuresis was quite accidental. It was way back in 1904 that Pfoundler, a pediatrician, developed an apparatus very similar to Mowrer's later technique, and used it simply to warn the nursing staff that a child had wet the bed and needed attention. The therapeutic effects of the apparatus were not anticipated.

Aversive conditioning procedures and Wolpe's reciprocal inhibition, or counter-conditioning, methods were also empirical developments. I agree with Professor Hammer that Guthrie must be given credit for the early development of desensitization procedures. His toleration technique, for example, can be described as a desensitization method. Wolpe's essential contribution was to show that relaxation can be a very effective antagonist of anxiety, and can be utilized therapeutically. Wolpe has made other contributions, but the essential point here is that the procedure of counter-conditioning was first tried purely on the basis of analogy with animal behaviour. Of course, refinements have been introduced as a result of more recent studies of learning, but

I must agree with Professor Yates that it is quite misleading to describe behaviour therapy as the application of modern learning theory. The fact is that the application of behaviour therapy involves us in a minimum of theoretical assumptions.

Nevertheless, it is widely recognized that the case for behaviour therapy would be strengthened if it could be shown that its procedures may be derived rationally from a theory of the etiology of behaviour disorders. Accordingly, several authors have attempted to develop a rational basis for behaviour therapy. The theoretical assumptions formulated by Eysenck are probably the most explicit. These assumptions may be summarized as follows.

Disregarding disorders that can be conceived of as habit deficiencies, all neurotic behaviours consist of maladaptive conditioned responses of the autonomic nervous system, or of skeletal responses which reduce conditioned autonomic reactions. Secondly, maladaptive conditioned autonomic responses, such as anxiety or fear, are acquired by a process of classical conditioning in situations of strong excitation. Thirdly, maladaptive skeletal responses which reduce conditioned autonomic reactions are acquired by a process of instrumental conditioning. In other words, all behaviour disorders represent either a lack of conditioning or maladaptive conditioning.

As I have stated elsewhere,[11] I believe that this theoretical model gives a plausible account of the development of a number of behavioural disorders, e.g. certain phobias, certain obsessive-compulsive behaviours, and certain sexual deviations. On the other hand, I feel that interpretations of the more complex forms of disturbance in terms of maladaptive habits are not at all convincing.

Perhaps the crucial theoretical issue is whether or not there is a true continuity between the simpler and the more complex forms of behaviour disorder. The position of most behaviour therapy theorists on this issue is quite clear. Most would agree with the proposition that all behaviour disorders, like all "normal" forms of behaviour, are acquired, and may be changed, in accordance with the same reinforcement principles. From this point of view, every item of disturbed behaviour is theoretically explicable in terms of the "laws of learning". Interestingly enough, on this point the behaviourist's views run parallel with those of Freud, since Freud emphasized the continuity between the normal and the abnormal (or rather, between the abnormal and the normal!) and regarded all neurotic symptoms as solutions to problems. The Pavlovians, on the other hand, favour the discontinuity position. These workers make a sharp distinction between conditioned emotional reactions, no matter how inappropriately generalized, and neurotic "breakdown". The latter state is characterized by disturbances of "phasic" activity (e.g. stronger responses to weak stimuli than to strong stimuli, positive reactions to negative stimuli and vice versa), disappearance of recently acquired conditioning, and inability to elaborate relatively simple conditioned linkages.

Hebb is another experimentalist who has opted for the discontinuity hypothesis in the course of emphasizing the non-experiential determinants of behaviour disorders.

My own inclination is towards the discontinuity point of view, but I recognize that the onus is on those who take this stand to demonstrate its advantages for theory and practice. At the moment, a convincing demonstration cannot be offered, but I am confident that this is a temporary state of affairs.

Let me summarize what I have been attempting to say in this last section. I have argued that the essence of behaviour therapy, as it is at present practised, lies not in the application of a learning theory interpretation of the nature of behaviour disorders, but in the application of principles of behavioural control derived from experimental studies of normal behaviour, plus the use of experimental methods in the analysis of particular disorders and the evaluation of treatment. It follows that the use of behaviour therapy procedures does not necessarily involve us in the acceptance of a learning theory interpretation of the etiology of behaviour disorders. Certainly we must give up the idea that behaviour disorders are all surface indicators of underlying conflict. This idea must be given up if we are going to have any sort of respect for the facts, but we are not thereby compelled to accept the view that all behaviour disorders are acquired by processes of conditioning. The major theoretical issue is whether there is continuity between the simpler and the more complex behavioural disturbances. The behaviourists and the Freudians are alike in supporting the continuity position. Acceptance of the alternative discontinuity hypothesis, which I believe to be more plausible, obliges us to demonstrate, at some point, its advantages for practice.

REFERENCES

1. Lovibond, S.H. (1964). *Conditioning and enuresis*. Oxford: Pergamon.
2. Lovibond, S.H. & Coote, M.A. Enuresis. In *Symptoms of psychopathology* (ed. C.G. Costello). New York: Wiley, in press.
3. Wolpe, J. (1958). *Psychotherapy by reciprocal inhibition*. Stanford: Stanford University Press.
4. Cooper, J.E. (1963). A study of behaviour therapy in thirty psychiatric patients. *Lancet* 1, 411-15.

5. Cooper, J.E., Gelder, M.G. & Marks, I.M. (1965). Results of behaviour therapy in seventy-seven psychiatric patients. *Br. med. J.* **1**, 1222-25.
6. Feldman, M.P. (1966). Aversion therapy for sexual deviations: a critical review. *Psychol. Bull.* **65**, 65-79.
7. Ferster, C.B. & De Meyer, M.K. (1964). The development of performance in autistic children in an automatically controlled environment. In *Experiments in behaviour therapy* (ed. H. J. Eysenck). London: Pergamon.
8. Lang, P.J., Lazovik, A.D. & Reynolds, D.J. (1965). Desensitization suggestibility and pseudotherapy. *J. abnorm. soc. Psychol.* **70**, 395-402.
9. Rachman, S. (1965). Studies in desensitization. I. The separate effects of relaxation and desensitization. *Behav. Res. Ther.* **3**, 245-51.
10. Cautela, J.R. (1966). A behaviour therapy approach to pervasive anxiety. *Behav. Res. Ther.* **4**, 99-109.
11. Lovibond, S.H. (1966). The current status of behaviour therapy. *Can. Psychologist* **7**, 93-101.

SEMINAR ONE : PAPER THREE

Professor F. A. Whitlock

THE PROBLEM OF TREATMENT

The clinical psychiatrist treating adults is faced by a large number of persons suffering from a wide variety of behavioural disorders and mental disturbances. He knows that in a proportion of these patients purely physical methods of treatment will lead to the suppression of symptoms, although he should not delude himself into believing that physical methods of treatment alone cure anything. The forces of nature, the natural history of the disease and prolonged supportive psychotherapy may be the tools which produce improvement. Nevertheless, it has to be admitted that these techniques are both uncertain, time-consuming, and in other respects unsatisfactory.

The other main technique of treatment consists of psychotherapy, ranging from full psychoanalysis to simple supportive and counselling therapy. It has yet to be demonstrated clearly that psychotherapy produces the effects claimed for it. Nevertheless, those of us who do practise this particular technique feel that, on occasions, changes occur which would not have occurred had that treatment not been applied. However, once again the treatment is uncertain, it is time-consuming, it is applicable only to a small number of patients and, in the very nature of things, can hardly be carried out on an individual basis by busy hospital psychiatrists required to treat large numbers of patients in somewhat unsatisfactory circumstances.

Compared with general medicine, there is no equivalent in psychiatry to penicillin treatment for acute infections. It may well be that this utopian state of affairs will never come about and

29

understandably we look with interest upon any new form of treatment which offers some hope that relief will be available for our patients and that the duration of treatment will be reasonably brief. We need to discover techniques of treatment for mental disorders which will be short, effective, do not harm the patient and do not require elaborate and time-consuming techniques. It has been claimed that behaviour therapy in its various forms goes some way to meeting these requirements. It is my purpose in this discussion to examine some of these claims without paying too much attention to the theoretical foundations upon which they rest.

THE CLASSES OF BEHAVIOUR THERAPY

As we have already heard, there are many types of behaviour therapy now available. For the purposes of discussion I propose to limit myself to the deconditioning and conditioning therapies whether operant or aversive. The deconditioning therapies are based largely upon the graded exposure of patients to anxiety-provoking situations and objects, while by relaxation, hypnosis, suggestion and encouragement, the therapist gets the patient to accept the situation without the development of anxiety. Over a period of time it is claimed that the unwanted phobic or anxious response disappears and that the patient loses his symptoms. In operant and aversive conditioning the principles involved seem to consist of the rewarding of desirable responses and the punishing of undesirable ones.

THE RESULTS OF BEHAVIOUR THERAPY

The protagonists for this form of treatment have reported enthusiastically upon their results. In particular the names of Wolpe, Lazarus and Eysenck stand out as persons who have gone far to demonstrate satisfactory results which, they claim, are superior to those obtained by conventional forms of psychotherapy. Unfortunately, many of the earlier and larger studies lack controls and adequate follow-up studies, so it is not always easy to assess these findings satisfactorily. For example, the claim by Wolpe[1] that over 90 per cent of his patients made satisfactory recoveries needs to be looked at with considerable caution as no other worker in this field has achieved success rates of this magnitude.

As time has gone by it has become evident that whereas certain classes of mental illness respond well to behaviour therapy, there is no clear indication that this form of treatment is a therapeutic panacea for all forms of mental illness. It has been applied to practically every form of behaviour disorder known to psychiatrists, but for the most part it has been used for the control of neurotic symptoms, particularly phobic symptoms and for the treatment of tics, obsessional disorders and enuresis. In addition, the aversive therapies have been used for the control of socially undesirable behaviour, notably sexual perversions and abnormalities, alcoholism and drug addiction.

The earlier writers on behaviour therapy were enthusiastic and a little uncritical, but in more recent times better designed studies with adequate follow-up and control data have indicated that whereas simple phobics respond extremely well to behaviour therapy, other forms of mental illness do not show such satisfactory results. I refer particularly to the studies of Cooper[2] and of Marks and Gelder,[3,4] who in a number of papers reported upon follow-up studies on patients treated at the Maudsley Hospital in London. These findings have been summarized by the authors in a paper[5] which reported upon 77 cases matched with 55 control subjects. All of the index cases had at least five treatments of behaviour therapy which was based upon training, desensitization, relaxation and avoidance learning. The 77 cases were composed of 29 agoraphobics, 12 other phobics, 10 obsessionals, 13 with writer's cramp and 13 miscellaneous classes of neurotic symptoms. Immediate findings show that 61 per cent of those treated by behaviour therapy improved compared with 44 per cent of the controls. At the end of one year 29 per cent of the behaviour therapy group were much improved compared with 22 per cent of the controls. What stands out particularly from this paper are the poor results obtained by behaviour therapy with patients suffering from writer's cramp and obsessional rituals. By contrast, good results were obtained with patients suffering from simple phobic states but agoraphobics did not do particularly well. The authors remarked that behaviour therapy is not a particularly brief form of treatment and that as far as their agoraphobics were concerned, 56 sessions were given over a period of six months, compared with 27 sessions over a period of four months for the other phobics.

This paper reached conclusions which to some extent had already been given in earlier papers by these authors. It was pointed out that the more complex the problem is, the less satisfactory was the response. It was also observed that in a number of cases the combination of supportive psychotherapy with behaviour therapy seemed to be the ideal to be aimed at, a remark which is echoed by Meyer and Crisp[6] in a recent paper. In short, it is

31

necessary in psychiatry to treat people as well as symptoms, a point which is sometimes overlooked by the psychologist, who is more concerned with the alteration of an unwanted piece of behaviour by the application of a particular technique. Nevertheless, in psychiatry we know perfectly well that the individual personality plays an important part in the production of symptoms and that failure to take note of premorbid personality attributes often leads to poor results or relapse. It follows, therefore, that treatment confined to the application of learning theory to the solution of our patients' behaviour disorders will not help more than a small number of patients whose disturbances are mainly monosymptomatic phobias.

The qualities of behaviour therapy

It has to be asked how far the claims of the behaviour therapists have been substantiated and how far the treatment techniques fulfil the requirements already mentioned, that the treatment should be brief, effective, harmless and relatively simple to apply.

The problem of available time in psychiatry is one of those perennial vexations from which none of us can escape. We are always searching for a brief form of treatment which will not take up too much of the psychiatrist's and, for that matter, of the patient's time. Hence our reliance, too greatly in my opinion, on drugs and other forms of physical treatment, largely because these are brief even though they may not be particularly effective. The evidence obtained from the studies of Wolpe, Lazarus, and Marks and Gelder does little to support the view that behaviour therapy techniques are less time-consuming than conventional psychotherapy. In fact, in the paper presented by Marks and Gelder[3] agoraphobics were given a mean number of 4.1 sessions per week of behaviour therapy whereas controls received only 2.4 sessions per week of conventional psychotherapy. There is some evidence to suggest that the more frequent sessions produced a slightly higher level of improvement but certainly these findings do not support the view that behaviour therapy is less time-consuming than psychotherapy. The duration of treatment for the agoraphobics was 5.4 months, for the other phobias 4.5 months and for controls 3.8 months. In the end there was little to choose between the controls and agoraphobics but undoubtedly the straightforward phobics did very much better than the controls.

In Wolpe's original series without controls or follow-up the mean period of treatment was 10.7 months and the mean number of interviews 45.6. Again, there is little to support the view that behaviour therapy is a brief form of treatment, even though Lazarus[7] in a later report managed to obtain recovery rates in around 60 per cent of patients with a mean of 15 sessions for his patients.

RESULTS IN VARIOUS CLASSES OF MENTAL ILLNESS

There seems to be little doubt that behaviour therapy is remarkably effective for simple phobias. Less satisfactory results have been obtained with other forms of neurosis and somewhat conflicting reports have been submitted on behaviour disorders, although individual case reports have shown that certain classes of sexual perversion can respond well to aversion therapy. The other condition claimed to respond successfully is alcoholism. Once again, examination of the literature shows all too clearly that the degree, duration and quality of the response varies very considerably. The more highly motivated the patient, the better the premorbid personality, the better the general background, the better will be the final outcome for the treatment of alcoholism by aversion therapy. However, at this stage there is no clear indication that this form of treatment offers anything better than that provided by conventional forms of group or individual psychotherapy coupled with such drugs as Antabuse.

THE TECHNIQUES OF TREATMENT

The more one reads about the various forms of behaviour therapy, the more clear it becomes that each patient has to be treated as an individual and that in a good many instances the use of apparatus, objects, or situations makes major claims upon the time of the individual therapist. For example, agoraphobics need to be accompanied by their therapists during their walks in the street. Patients suffering from specific phobias have to be given graded exposure to the stimulus object, but once again the handling of such objects does not always lend itself easily to the therapeutic situation. Whatever the theoretical background might be for the use of these techniques, a further disadvantage is the difficulty of obtaining generalization of response outside the clinical situation. In short, one might well develop a satisfactory aversion or deconditioning within the consulting room or clinic, only to find that the same result does not persist once the patient moves into the outside world.

THE ETHICS OF BEHAVIOUR THERAPY

It has to be said that a great deal of the work hitherto reported in this field has been in the hands of clinical psychologists who are not responsible for the care and management of the patient. Ultimate responsibility must rest with the individual clinician, whether or not he applies this particular form of treatment himself. This fact alone raises ethical issues not often raised at conferences of this nature. Nevertheless, a number of commentators have touched upon the matter and Holden[8] in particular had some pertinent points to make concerning the ethical aspects of this form of treatment.

I do not think that anyone would have any quarrel with the application of techniques of deconditioning by reciprocal inhibition, anxiety reduction and relaxation. On the other hand, it is extremely difficult in my view — and in the view of others — to distinguish between what is politely referred to as "aversive deconditioning" and simple punishment. The fact that the aversion methods of treatment are particularly applied to those forms of behaviour regarded by society as undesirable lends point to my contention that such forms of treatment can only be described as punishment, even though administered scientifically and disguised by scientific jargon. I think we should ask ourselves how far we should be punishing our patients and how far we succeed by these techniques in relieving suffering. Holden's view was that the task of the doctor is to relieve suffering in the individual patient. Whether or not he has a duty to society to prevent crime or, for that matter, to treat antisocial behaviour not necessarily of a criminal kind, is a vexed issue which brings in matters of moral and value judgments. The techniques involved, particularly in the treatment of sexual deviation, would appear to some persons distasteful. I am not suggesting for one moment that the conscious motives of those who apply these techniques are anything but reputable, but I would suggest that before we expose homosexuals to homosexual stimulus objects and subject the patients to electric shocks whenever erotic arousal takes place, we should ask ourselves what our precise role in this situation is. How far, in fact, are we ministering to the needs of our patients and how far are we bending our patients in order to get them to conform to social expectations? I would submit that as doctors this is not our role and that it is a role which we take on at some danger to ourselves. One of Holden's homosexual patients said to him, "If they can do this to me, if they can force me against my conscious inclinations to change my sexual orientation from men to women, what is to

34

prevent them changing it to cows?" The answer, of course, is the humanity and common sense of the investigator but I am not so trustful of human nature that I can believe implicitly that no investigator in the name of science might not one day do just that in order to see what would happen.

McGuire and Vallance[9] treated a number of patients using electric shock to produce aversion. One of these cases was a twenty-five-year-old fetishist who masturbated to the accompaniment of masochistic fantasies. At the end of eight weeks of treatment with electric shock aversion therapy, he masturbated to heterosexual fantasies for the first time in his life. Neither of these investigators seems to have asked himself whether this was really an improvement upon the original state of affairs, neither do they appear to have enquired into the effects of the treatment upon the man's sexual life as a whole. The techniques of aversion therapy include the production of nausea and vomiting, the administration of painful electric shocks, and the induction of intense fear as a result of apnoea produced by succinyl choline injections. Such procedures seem far removed from the humanitarian ideal of medical treatment. I would like to suggest to this audience that we should pay more attention to the ethical factors involved in the application of these techniques. I feel that aversion therapy should not be in our therapeutic armamentarium, partly because it is not always effective but also because the means do not justify the ends even when those ends are satisfactory from the social point of view. It is not our task to make our patients conform to social expectations which vary from time to time depending upon the law and the climate of public opinion. It is our task to relieve suffering and I cannot see that aversion therapy does anything except inflict suffering in the name of some vague ideal which is rarely defined.

It is sometimes argued that surgical treatment involves infliction of pain in order to produce a cure and that this is no different from the pain inflicted by the behaviour therapist. This is a false analogy as no surgeon of my acquaintance deliberately sets out to inflict pain as a therapeutic technique. In fact he uses anaesthesia and pain-relieving drugs with the expressed intention of reducing or relieving pain.

SUMMARY

I would like to summarize the foregoing comments by saying that for the time being at least the clinical psychiatrist should continue to show an interest in behaviour therapy and even welcome its use for the management and treatment of certain specific forms of mental illness. It seems to be remarkably successful for simple phobias but for the more complex types of neurotic disturbance it has been less successful. It may well be that the combination of psychotherapy with behaviour therapy could be the form of treatment which ultimately will obtain the most satisfactory results. It is my personal view that aversion therapy is not a type of treatment we should be employing. The long history of psychiatry is punctuated by outbreaks of minor violence against patients, all done with the best of intentions, in the hope that such methods will lead to change in the patient's behaviour. I suggest that current preoccupation with aversion therapy is just another of those outbreaks and that the sooner it is recognized as such the better for all concerned.

These strictures, of course, do not apply to reciprocal inhibition, relaxation, and graded deconditioning, introduced by Wolpe. Nevertheless, it is perfectly evident that behaviour therapy is not a short-cut type of treatment. It is time-consuming and, at times, difficult and elaborate. The better the motivation of the patient the better will be the outcome and this is something which applies to all forms of mental illness and all forms of treatment. I am very well satisfied that behaviour therapy has a part to play in the overall management of mental illness. Nevertheless, I am sceptical about the more extreme claims made on behalf of this type of treatment, just as I am sceptical about any 90 per cent cure rate whether produced by psychotherapy, behaviour therapy, or drugs. In the last analysis I am bound to admit that behaviour therapy has not yet come up with the form of treatment for which we are all seeking. It may well be that this is something which cannot be achieved owing to the very complexity of human mental functioning. It is probably quite misleading to compare and apply the techniques found to be effective on laboratory rats to human neurotic patients. The circumstances in the human patient are so infinitely more complex that I am doubtful whether a simple learning theory can really explain the whole basis of neurosis. For that reason also I am doubtful whether behaviour therapy as such will provide the full answer for all forms of mental illness. It is clearly most effective in those circumstances where learning theory appears to have an immediate and ready application. Nevertheless, despite these over-cautious and critical comments, I hope that before long behaviour therapy will be available in this University Department of Psychiatry and that its application to selected patients will lead to improvement in their mental well-being.

REFERENCES

1. Wolpe, J. (1958). *Psychotherapy by reciprocal inhibition.* Stanford: Stanford University Press.
2. Cooper, J.E. (1963). A study of behaviour therapy in thirty psychiatric patients. *Lancet* **1**, 411-15.
3. Marks, I.M. & Gelder, M.G. (1965). A controlled retrospective study of behaviour therapy in phobic patients. *Br. J. Psychiat.* **111**, 561-73.
4. Gelder, M.G. & Marks, I.M. (1966). Severe agoraphobia: a controlled prospective trial of behaviour therapy. *Br. J. Psychiat.* **112**, 309-19.
5. Cooper, J.E., Gelder, M.G. & Marks, I.M. (1965). Results of behaviour therapy in seventy-seven psychiatric patients. *Br. med. J.* **1**, 1222-25.
6. Meyer, V. & Crisp, A.H. (1966). Some problems in behaviour therapy. *Br. J. Psychiat.* **112**, 367-81.
7. Lazarus, A.A. (1963). The results of behaviour therapy in 126 cases of severe neurosis. *Behav. Res. Ther.* **1** (1), 69-80.
8. Holden, H.M. (1965). Should aversion and behaviour therapy be used in the treatment of delinquency? *Br. J. Crim.* **5**, 377-87.
9. McGuire, R.J. & Vallance, M. (1964). Aversion therapy by electric shock: a simple technique. *Br. med. J.* **1**, 151-53.

DISCUSSION

Professor Yates: I must say that I don't share Dr. Lovibond's optimism about technology in behaviour therapy. Professor Hammer made the point, with which I entirely agree, that our knowledge in general about human behaviour at present can only be described, charitably, as rudimentary at the best. And this is necessarily so, given the extraordinary complexity of human behaviour. I simply don't see how, in the light of our general knowledge of human behaviour, scientifically speaking, we can expect to be able to control, manipulate and change the complex behaviour of disturbed people.

I also think that the only way in which we can proceed here is by an intermarriage of theory and technique, with each reflecting on the other. Indeed, I always quote as an outstanding example of this, in the field of behaviour therapy, Dr. Lovibond's own contribution[1] in the field of enuresis, where we originally had a technique, the Mowrer technique, and a theory, Mowrer's theory, which appeared to complement each other almost perfectly for twenty years. And then Dr. Lovibond came along and said, "Mowrer's theory cannot possibly be correct", and formulated an alternative theory, and from that derived a different, or at least modified, method of treatment. Leaving aside the question of the individual case, rather than groups, this seems to me to be precisely the ideal that we are striving for in the field of behaviour therapy.

With regard to Professor Whitlock's comments, I entirely agree with a lot of what he said, particularly about the problem of ethics, but this problem of course isn't peculiar to behaviour therapy. One need only mention the still prevalent use of insulin treatment, electric shock treatment, and so forth, which have been imposed upon literally millions of people over the last twenty or thirty years. I don't think the question of ethics is different in the case of behaviour therapy from its bearing on the case of psychiatry in general.

One last point. Professor Whitlock said that we must always remember that we deal with people, with the person. Now this is true, except that I can never quite understand what is meant when we say that we deal with the person, because when we deal with a person we must have something to deal with, and that something is behaviour. We can't do anything with a patient unless he himself does something. Let me give you a simple example. There is a common phrase which says "sometimes I sit and think, and sometimes I just sit". How do you distinguish between a patient who is just sitting, and one who is sitting and thinking, unless he performs some kind of activity, or unless you can note some internal process such as EEG changes and so on? We must deal with *behaviour*. To talk about dealing with the *person* means that we are dealing with certain aspects of his *behaviour*. I entirely agree with Professor Whitlock's criticism that psychologists have tended until now to deal with patients in very restricted situations of the laboratory. This was inevitable, but recent work by Lazarus[2] and others shows very clearly how we have to try now, more and more, to move out of the laboratory into the real life situation. Lazarus has shown, for example, that with a phobic patient, if you simply treat the phobia in a restricted situation, you may buy yourself a whole heap of trouble because, if the phobia disappears, what happens then is that family relationships become interrupted, because the family has adjusted to the phobia. Similarly, Gavin Andrews[3] in Sydney has pointed out the fact that families often get upset if you eliminate a stutter in a person, particularly if that person has always stuttered, because the family has adjusted to the person's stutter and knows how to deal with him as a stutterer. Once he loses his stutter, and begins to talk all the time, as he apparently does, ths can be extremely disturbing to the family. So clearly we would agree that one of the grave deficiencies of behaviour therapy at the present time is this tendency to remain in the laboratory. We must try and move out of the laboratory into the real life situation.

Dr. Shearer: It would be interesting to know where the behaviour therapists derive their supply of patients with monosymptomatic disorders. I'm not disputing the fact that many patients have phobias which can trouble them. But in my experience as a medical practitioner, very few patients who come to me complain of monosymptomatic disorders.

Dr. Lovibond: One point that I think can be made here is that many of the people who have had specific phobias treated by desensitization techniques have had other symptoms. It is true that, for the purpose of experimental studies, essentially normal people with phobic fears of snakes or spiders have been sought out, but many of the clinical patients who have been treated for phobic reactions have had other sorts of behavioural disturbances as well. As I pointed out earlier, however, it is possible to work on the phobias without changing the other symptoms. A friend of mine in a psychiatric hospital in England made a survey of all the patients in that hospital, and he decided that something like 55 per cent had disorders which would have been amenable to treatment by reciprocal inhibition techniques. In other words, they had some sort of phobic symptoms in their total symptomatic picture. It is true then that monosymptomatic disorders are rare.

Dr. Nurcombe: I would like to put a question to Dr. Lovibond. Are you aware of the work of Crisp[4] published in the *British Journal of Medical Psychology*, on the relationship between transference, improvement in behaviour therapy and symptom emergence, following behaviour therapy, using Kelly's grid technique to measure transference?

Dr. Lovibond: No, I missed that one.

Dr. Nurcombe: The suggestion was that patients with more positive transference at the beginning of treatment did better, also that as transference became more positive the symptoms improved. Transference is relevant to improvement in therapy.

Dr. Lovibond: Well, no one is going to assert that if the patient hasn't some sort of positive relationship with the therapist, he is going to do as well as the person who has. While I wouldn't agree with Professor Whitlock's view of the ethics of the situation, it is obvious that in order to get a person to go through the sorts of procedures which, if not uncomfortable or painful, can be extremely tedious, you must develop a high degree of motivation in him. How can you do this other than by establishing the ordinary sort of positive relationship with the person? Other than this, I don't think it has any bearing on the outcome of the specific procedures.

Dr. B. Klug: I'd like to query Dr. Lovibond's comments on enuresis. In child guidance practice, it is most uncommon for a child to have monosymptomatic enuresis. Secondly, very often enuresis decreases without any specific treatment if the underlying conflict can be isolated, and the other behaviour disorders treated successfully. Thirdly, we have found that Tofranil, an antidepressant drug, is very useful in coping with enuresis. I would not be so rash as to claim a 90 per cent cure, but I will claim that a large proportion of children have been treated quite successfully. How does Dr. Lovibond reconcile these findings in the light of his work with behaviour therapy?

Dr. Lovibond: Your first question concerned the frequency with which children appear in child guidance clinics suffering only from enuresis. When I became interested in enuresis, I decided that what I had to do at all costs was to avoid the child guidance clinics as a source of subjects. It seemed to me that children attending clinics were highly selected cases, and I came to the conclusion that it was very rare indeed for a mother to bring a child into a guidance clinic simply because he was enuretic.

Normally, the child would have other behavioural symptoms as well, and the fact that he was enuretic would be disclosed in the interview. So, for my work, I set about finding a more representative sample of enuretics. I did this by making approaches through my student groups, and I was able to find many enuretics who had never been to a guidance clinic, although quite a number of parents had discussed the disorder with a general practitioner. My own results, and the results of several other studies that have been reported subsequently, show clearly that an unselected group of enuretics is very little more disturbed generally than a comparable group of non-enuretics. It is true that you get occasional children in whom enuresis is only one of a complex of symptoms. I would suggest that these are the children who are commonly seen in clinics, and they are very unrepresentative of the enuretics in the general community. The figures I was quoting relate specifically to samples of enuretics that can be regarded as representative of the total population of enuretics. I've had the impression that enuretics with other symptoms are more difficult to treat than run of the mill enuretics, but in most cases the enuresis has responded and left the rest of the symptoms intact.

On the second point. We know of course that there is a considerable degree of spontaneous recovery in enuresis. There have been enough surveys now to allow us to establish a reasonable estimate of the incidence of enuresis in the general community. The incidence curve drops from the first year of life, at first rapidly, and then less rapidly, to reach a virtual asymptote at around fourteen or fifteen years of age. It is true then that, particularly in the lower age groups, a child who is enuretic is very likely not to be enuretic some years later. However, when I speak of an arrest rate of 90 per cent, this has to be compared with an estimated spontaneous recovery rate of the order of 4 per cent during the treatment period. Recently there have been several experimental studies which have included untreated control groups, and the rate of recovery in these groups is almost identical with that estimated from the age incidence curve.

Now on the question of the effects of Tofranil. Most investigators using this drug have reported that the disorder can be suppressed as long as the drug is being administered, but as soon as the drug is withdrawn the child tends to relapse. If you go on long enough, of course, you'll pick up a few spontaneous recoveries. There has been one recent study in which the technique of gradually tapering off the dose has been used, and the claim has been made that using this procedure prevents reversion to enuresis when the drug is withdrawn. This is the first study to report this effect, and, if the results can be replicated, it will be an important development in the drug therapy of enuresis. I would agree that Tofranil is the only drug which at present has even the slightest chance of taking the place of conditioning treatment.

REFERENCES

1. Lovibond, S.H. (1964). *Conditioning and enuresis.* Oxford: Pergamon.
2. Lazarus, A. (1966). Broad-spectrum behaviour therapy and the treatment of agoraphobia. *Behav. Res. Ther.* **4**, 95-97.
3. Andrews, G. Personal communication.
4. Crisp, A.H. (1966). "Transference", "symptom emergence" and "social repercussion" in behaviour therapy: a study of fifty-four treated patients. *Br. J. med. Psychol.* **39**, 179-96.

SEMINAR TWO: CASE STUDIES IN BEHAVIOUR THERAPY

SEMINAR TWO: **PAPER ONE**

Aversion Therapy in the Treatment of Male Homosexuals

Dr. N. McConaghy

This paper reports an attempt to investigate the value of two forms of aversion therapy in the treatment of male homosexuality. Penile plethysmography was used as an index of response to treatment. Freund[1] originally investigated the measurement of penile volume change to the sight of nude males and females as a measure of sexual orientation and he found it to be highly valid. He used a rather elaborate penile attachment.[2] We employed a simpler one (Figure 1). The blind end of a fingerstall was cut off and the cut-end stretched over the open end of a cylindrical tin of approximately $2\frac{1}{4}$ in. diameter and $3\frac{1}{2}$ in. length. A nipple was soldered into the closed end of the tin and connected by a plastic tube to a standard Grass pressure transducer. The penis was inserted into the tin through the open end of the fingerstall, which maintained an air-tight connection.

Freund used still photographs of nudes. In the present study, the nudes were presented in moving pictures of ten seconds duration. The activities they carried out were not designed to be sexually provocative, as it was considered that this could limit the type of person to whom the film could be shown. Behaviour such as hair-combing, towelling and taking off items of clothing was employed. The filmed segments of nudes were incorporated in a travelogue type movie film of London and its environs. Ten photographs of young adult women and ten of young adult men were shown alternately at minute intervals. The photographs of the women were preceded by photographs of a red circle, those of the men by photographs of a green triangle. These figures were shown for ten seconds. They were inserted to produce conditional responses to the unconditional stimuli of the nudes.

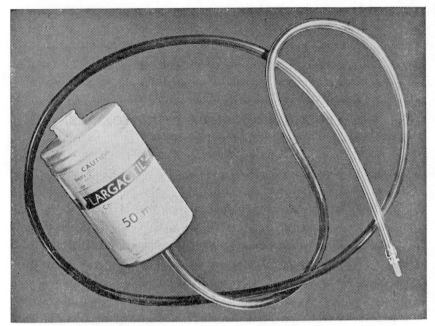

Fig. 1. Apparatus for measuring penile volume change.

While the subject viewed the film, a Grass 5D polygraph was employed to record continuously changes in his penile volume, his psychogalvanic response and the time of presentation of the conditional and unconditional stimuli. A segment of a typical record of a heterosexual subject is shown in Figure 2.

QUANTIFICATION OF THE PENILE VOLUME CHANGE

Freund exposed each picture for thirteen seconds, with an interval of nineteen seconds between pictures. He used as a measure of response the greatest negative or positive deflection occurring during the presentation of each picture, taking as a base-line the level at the beginning of the picture. When a positive and a negative value appeared together, which Freund found to occur only rarely, the negative value was subtracted from the positive. In the present study a negative and a positive deflection occurred frequently during the presentation of the nudes. For this reason the difference in the level of the penile plethysomograph at the onset and termination of the photographs of the nudes was used as a measure of the response. When it was necessary to change the calibration of the polygraph during the record, the

measurement of the difference in levels was multiplied or divided
by the appropriate figure, so that the final scores were such as
would have been obtained had the calibration remained unaltered.
An increase in volume was scored as positive and a decrease as
negative. This gave ten scores for the volume change to the males
and ten for the volume change to the females for each subject.
The statistical significance of the difference of these two sets of
scores could then be calculated using the Mann-Whitney test.

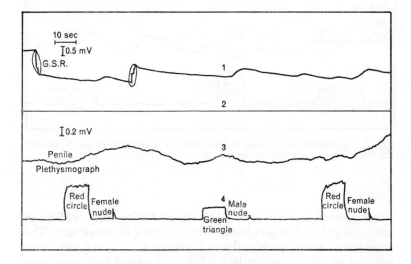

Fig. 2. Typical heterosexual response. The first graph is the GSR, the third
the penile plethysmograph and the fourth the indicator as to what stimuli are
being shown. The large maintained deflection accompanies the red circle, the
following portion of the graph to the brief deflection, the female nude. The
lesser maintained deflection accompanies the green triangle and the following
portion of the graph to the brief deflection, the male nude.

Freund apparently regarded a negative or a positive deflection
as an equally significant response. This procedure was followed
in part. When the means of the responses to both males and females
were positive, the mean which was higher was taken as indicating
the sexual orientation of the subject. When one mean was positive
and one negative, the positive mean was taken as indicating the
sexual orientation, irrespective of the values of the two means.
When both means were negative, the mean which was greater was
taken as indicating the sexual orientation. A segment of a record
of a homosexual subject showing this type of response is shown
in Figure 3.

47

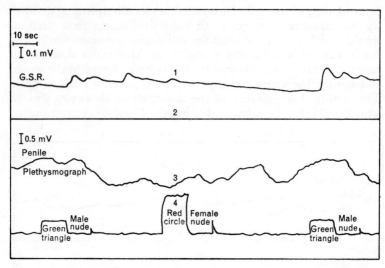

Fig. 3. Record of homosexual subject showing a response of penile volume decrease to both male and female nudes.

SUBJECTS

All persons conscious of homosexual feeling who wished to have this reduced or eliminated were accepted for treatment. The response of thirty such patients is reported. The majority were referred by other psychiatrists. Their ages ranged from seventeen to forty-one with a median age of twenty-five. Five were less than twenty-one years old; five were married, of whom the youngest was twenty-eight; fourteen had a police record for homosexual behaviour — two had been arrested but not prosecuted; seven had one conviction; two, two convictions; two, three convictions, and one, five convictions. Only two of the thirty patients were under threat of conviction when they came for treatment. Thirteen considered they were sexually aroused by women, or had been in the past; four of these thirteen considered their heterosexual interest was stronger than their homosexual interest. These four had all been arrested for homosexual behaviour — one on three occasions; two of these four were married and the other two stated they had inhibitions about having intercourse with women. Ten stated they were not sexually aroused by women and had shown no significant heterosexual interest. Seven were uncertain or stated they were not sexually aroused by women but had had girl friends at some period and one of these was married. He and another

48

married man had ceased heterosexual intercourse some years previously. The other three married men were having regular intercourse with their wives. Of the non-married patients, five had had heterosexual intercourse on one to ten occasions, and two others had attempted this. Twenty-eight of the thirty patients had had homosexual relations with a number of partners. Two had no overt homosexual experience apart from mutual masturbation in early adolescence. One of these two developed strong emotional attractions to other males and the other was distressed by homosexual sadistic fantasies. Neither had any heterosexual desire or experience.

The thirty patients were randomly allotted to one of two forms of aversion therapy — apomorphine and aversion-relief therapy. Both these methods have been utilized by other workers to treat homosexuality and both were planned so that they could be regularly administered in a general hospital psychiatric unit without being excessively demanding of staff time. Both required five days' hospitalization.

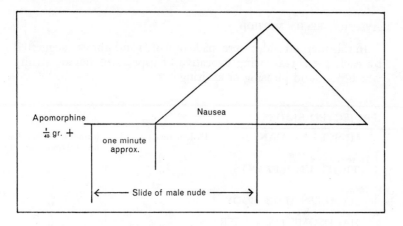

Fig. 4. Apomorphine avoidance therapy sequence.

APOMORPHINF AVERSION THERAPY

This was carried out as illustrated in Figure 4. Initially 1/40 gr. apomorphine was administered by sub-cutaneous injection, and after a period a slide of a nude or semi-nude male was projected on the wall of the room within the patient's vision. If the nausea was not sufficiently unpleasant, the dose was increased with subsequent injections. Severe nausea lasting ten minutes was considered satisfactory. The patient was requested to attempt to respond to the slide with a feeling of sexual arousal and to facilitate this was left alone to carry out the treatment, apart from a few initial supervisory visits. The patient timed the onset of nausea to each injection with a stop-watch and after the subsequent injection turned on the projector one minute before this time. This was to arrange as far as possible that the conditioned stimulus (the picture of the male and the patient's associated homosexual fantasies) preceded the onset of the unconditioned response (the nausea). The projector was turned off shortly before the nausea reaction was at its worst so that its termination would not coincide with relief from the diminution of this response.

Each injection was associated with a change of slide. About fifteen different slides were used with each patient. Each patient received treatment on five consecutive days, receiving four injections on the first day and six on subsequent days, a total of twenty-eight injections.

AVERSION-RELIEF METHOD

In this method slides were made of words and phrases suggested by each patient as being evocative of aspects of homosexuality which he found pleasing or exciting.

PROJECTED SLIDES			
	MUSCULAR MAN	Patient reads aloud:	immediately receives painful shock to fingers
	10 secs. TIGHT UNDERPANTS	,,	,,
14 such slides	*10 secs.* HAIRLESS MALE BODY ETC.	,,	,,
	HANDSOME TEEN-AGER	,,	,,
	10 secs. WOMAN'S FIGURE	,,	No shock—relief
5 such sequences with 2½ minute intervals between = 1 session. 3 sessions given daily.			

Fig. 5. Aversion-relief therapy sequence.

These slides were used on the plan shown in Figure 5. Fourteen homosexual type slides were projected at ten second intervals.

The patient was instructed to read each one aloud. Immediately he finished reading each phrase he received a painful electric shock through electrodes attached to the fingers. The level of shock was such as to produce a marked flinch reaction and the patient was told it was to be painful, but not unbearable. The shocks were delivered through a Grass S4 stimulator with silver electrodes ⅜ in. diameter coated with electrode jelly and attached to the tip of two fingers with elastoplast strips. Each stimulus was of one second duration and consisted of one millisecond pulses delivered at the rate of 100 pulses per second. The voltage of stimulus was determined for each patient and varied from 30 to 140 volts.

Following the fourteen slides was one related to aspects of normal sexuality. This was left on for forty seconds and not punished. The appearance of this slide was accompanied by a sense of relief at the termination of the shocks. This procedure was carried out five times, with intervals of two and a half minutes between each series. The order of the fourteen slides was changed for each series so that the subjects did not learn to expect the final slide. A different final slide was used for each of the five series of presentations. Three such sessions were given daily for five consecutive days, so that a total of 1,050 shocks were administered.

Patients were assessed as to the degree of homosexual orientation indicated by penile plethysmography both before and after treatment, according to the experimental design shown in Table 1. This allowed the change in response to the film over a three week period without treatment intervening to be compared to the change over this period with treatment intervening.

TABLE 1. PLAN OF EXPERIMENT, SHOWING TREATMENT AND
CONTROL CONDITIONS

Treatment Group
Test I — Treatment 1 week — 2 weeks — Test II
Control Group
Test I — 3 weeks — Test II — Treatment 1 week — 2 weeks — Test III
Treatment = Apomorphine or Aversion-relief.

To aid in determining the validity of penile plethysmography as an indication of sexual orientation, the response of eleven heterosexual subjects to the film was also investigated. These subjects were medical students ranging in age from twenty to twenty-nine years. They were informed that they were to act as controls for homosexual subjects and only subjects who were not conscious of any homosexual feeling were asked to volunteer.

The means of their response scores are show in Table 2. All indicated heterosexual orientation and in all but one the differences in the responses to males and females were statistically significant. It will be noted that none showed a mean negative response to both sexes.

TABLE 2. PLETHYSMOGRAPHY RESPONSE OF HETEROSEXUAL SUBJECTS

SUB-JECT	AGE (YR)	PLETHYSMOGRAPHY RESPONSE			
		Mean response to female nudes	*Mean response to male nudes*	*Indicated sexual orientation*	*Statistical significance*
1	21	3·5	—1·4	Hetero.	$P < ·001$
2	29	3·2	—2·3	Hetero.	$P < ·001$
3	21	2·6	—0·3	Hetero.	$P < ·001$
4	20	1·3	—0·4	Hetero.	$P < ·001$
5	21	0·1	—1·1	Hetero.	$P < ·01$
6	21	0·5	—0·03	Hetero.	N.S.
7	26	3·3	—0·8	Hetero.	$P < ·001$
8	20	2·9	—1·3	Hetero.	$P < ·001$
9	21	3·0	—2·0	Hetero.	$P < ·001$
10	22	1·6	—0·4	Hetero.	$P < ·001$
11	21	5.5	—1·0	Hetero.	$P < ·001$

The responses of the control homosexuals at the initial assessment and the second assessment three weeks later are shown in Table 3. In the initial assessment, technically unsatisfactory records were obtained from two patients. Of the remaining fourteen, nine showed a homosexual orientation and five heterosexual. The U scores are those obtained by the Mann-Whitney test of significance. Those in italics indicate that the patient concerned showed mean negative response to both male and female nudes. In these cases, the positive and negative signs of the individual response scores were reversed to carry out the Mann-Whitney test so that a low U would continue to indicate a homosexual and a high U a heterosexual orientation. The sexual orientation indicated in the second assessment was the same for thirteen of the fourteen subjects, indicating a high degree of reliability for the test. Another index of the reliability is provided by the difference in the U scores of the two assessments. It will be seen that the difference is above sixteen in only one case, and the direction of the change is unrelated to the orientation indicated in the first assessment.

TABLE 3. CHANGE IN PENILE PLETHYSMOGRAPHY RESPONSE IN CONTROLS

| Patient | FIRST PRESENTATION | | | SECOND PRESENTATION | | | CHANGE | |
	U1 Orientation Significance			U2 Orientation Significance			U1–U2 Direction	
1	55	Heterosexual	N.S.	65.5	Heterosexual	N.S.	−10.5	Heterosexual
2				25	Homosexual	p < .05		
3	12.0	Homosexual	p < .01	24.5	Homosexual	p < .05	−12.5	Heterosexual
4	27	Homosexual	p < .05	11	Homosexual	p < .01	16	Homosexual
5	26	Homosexual	p < .05	28	Homosexual	N.S.	− 2	Heterosexual
6	16	Homosexual	p < .01	8.5	Homosexual	p < .001	7.5	Homosexual
7	80.5	Heterosexual	p < .05	77	Heterosexual	p < .05	3.5	Homosexual
8	13.5	Homosexual	p < .01	14	Homosexual	p < .01	− 0.5	Heterosexual
9	44	Homosexual	N.S.	28	Homosexual	N.S.	16	Homosexual
10		−		1.5	Homosexual	p < .001		
11	3	Homosexual	p < .001	76	Heterosexual	p < .05	−73	Heterosexual
12	82	Heterosexual	p < .01	87.5	Heterosexual	p < .01	− 5.5	Heterosexual
13	63	Heterosexual	N.S.	58	Heterosexual	N.S.	5	Homosexual
14	28.5	Homosexual	N.S.	21.5	Homosexual	p < .05	7	Homosexual
15	9	Homosexual	p < .001	2	Homosexual	p < .001	7	Homosexual
16	63	Heterosexual	N.S.	66	Heterosexual	N.S.	− 3	Heterosexual

TABLE 4. CHANGE IN PENILE PLETHYSMOGRAPHY RESPONSE IN
TREATMENT GROUP

| | FIRST PRESENTATION | | | SECOND PRESENTATION | | | CHANGE | |
	U1 Orientation Significance			U2 Orientation Significance			U1–U2 Direction	
Aversion-Relief Therapy								
1	13.5	Homosexual	p < .01	53	Heterosexual	N.S.	−39.5	Heterosexual
2	40.5	Homosexual	N.S.	56.5	Heterosexual	N.S.	−16	Heterosexual
3	5.5	Homosexual	p < .001	49	Heterosexual	N.S.	−43.5	Heterosexual
4		−		32.5	Heterosexual	N.S.		
5	11	Homosexual	p < .01	37	Homosexual	N.S.	−26	Heterosexual
6	36	Homosexual	N.S.	−		−		
7	0	Homosexual	p < .001	0	Homosexual	p < .001	0	−
Apomorphine Aversion Therapy								
8	59.5	Heterosexual	N.S.	9	Homosexual	p < .001	50.5	Homosexual
9	2.5	Homosexual	p < .001	36	Homosexual	N.S.	−33.5	Heterosexual
10	54	Heterosexual	N.S.	41.5	Homosexual	N.S.	12.5	Homosexual
11	51.5	?	N.S.	14.5	Homosexual	p < .01	37	Homosexual
12	31.5	Homosexual	N.S.	52.5	Heterosexual	N.S.	−21	Heterosexual
13	7.5	Homosexual	p < .001	45.5	Homosexual	N.S.	−38	Heterosexual
14	59	Heterosexual	N.S.	56.5	Heterosexual	N.S.	2.5	Homosexual

The responses of the treated subjects are shown in Table 4.
A technically unsatisfactory record was obtained from one patient
in the first assessment and one patient did not return for the second

53

assessment. In the initial assessment, nine of the thirteen showed a homosexual orientation, one indeterminate and three heterosexual. Again the italicized U scores indicate that the patients concerned showed a mean negative response to both male and female nudes. The sexual orientation indicated in the second assessment was the same in five, reversed in six and changed from indeterminate to homosexual in one. This change in orientation in seven of the twelve treated subjects compared with one of fourteen control subjects is statistically significant (Exact Test). However, it will be noted that the change in sexual orientation after treatment was to a homosexual orientation in two of the three patients showing a heterosexual orientation and in the one showing an indeterminate orientation in the initial assessment. The same trend is evident in the change in U scores for the two assessments in each treated subject. The direction of the change is invariably opposite to the orientation in the initial assessment. In the control group, it will be remembered that the direction of the change in orientation was unrelated to the orientation in the initial assessment. When the changes of U score for the two assessments in the treatment group are compared with those in the control group (Table 5), there is no significant difference in regard to direction of change, though there is a trend for the change to be in the direction of heterosexuality. However, if the finding is valid that the treatment is producing a trend towards reversal of the original orientation shown by the test, as more patients show a homosexual orientation at this time, more patients would show a change after treatment in the direction of heterosexuality. The variance in the difference in U scores in the treated group is clearly greater than in the control group.

From these findings the possibility must be considered that the aversion therapies of homosexuality utilized, rather than producing a definite shift in orientation towards heterosexuality, produce a less specific disturbance of sexual behaviour. One is reminded of Pavlov's finding of the production of the ultra-paradoxical phase when the nervous system of dogs was stressed in certain ways. In this phase the dog responded to positive conditional stimuli as if they were inhibitory and to inhibitory conditional stimuli as if they were positive. However, a simpler explanation would be that there is a reduction in sexual responsiveness with treatment, so that there is less discrimination in the response to males and females. With penile plethysmography in the controls (Table 3) there is no reduction in the number showing a statistically significant difference in response to male and female nudes. With the treatment group (Table 4) there is.

54

TABLE 5. CHANGE IN PENILE PLETHYSMOGRAPHY RESPONSE IN
TREATMENT AND CONTROL GROUPS (U_1-U_2)

Controls	Treatment Group
—73	—43.5
—12.5	—39.5
—10.5	—38
— 5.5	—33.5
— 3	—26
— 2	—21
— 0.5	—16
3.5	0
5	2.5
7	12.5
7	37
7.5	50.5
16	
16	

U = 61   N.S.

This concept of a general reduction in sexual responsiveness is
not entirely consistent with the short-term subjective change
reported by patients (Table 6). It will be noted that though a
number of patients considered their homosexual desire was
reduced, none felt that their heterosexual desire was reduced.
In fact, a number considered it increased. In the three married
patients having sexual relations with their wives there was no
reduction in heterosexual interest, and one reported a marked
increase.

TABLE 6. REPORTED CHANGE IN SEXUAL BEHAVIOUR TWO WEEKS
AFTER TREATMENT

APOMORPHINE AVERSION THERAPY		AVERSION-RELIEF THERAPY	
Homosexual	Heterosexual	Homosexual	Heterosexual
Desire Unchanged 3	Desire Unchanged 9(+2)	Desire Unchanged 8	Desire Unchanged 7
? Reduced 3	? Increased 1	? Reduced 1	? Increased 3
Reduced 6	Increased 3	Reduced 4	Increased 5
Nil 3		Nil 2	
Relations 1	Relations 3	Relations 6	Relations 0

With the apomorphine therapy, a greater number of patients
reported their homosexual desire reduced as compared with
aversion-relief. This was reflected in the reduced number of
patients with apomorphine continuing homosexual relations. With

55

aversion-relief, a greater number of patients reported an increased heterosexual interest. This apparent greater effectiveness of apomorphine as an aversive therapy compared with electric shock is in contrast to the many statements in the literature derived from theoretical considerations, which argue that the contrary would be true. The theoretical considerations are the variability in onset of the unpleasant effects of apomorphine as compared with the precise onset of electric shock and the central depressant effects of apomorphine.

I regret that insufficient time has elapsed to allow the presentation of adequate long-term follow-up data. My impression at the moment, for what it is worth, is that at a year following treatment, homosexual feeling is absent in about 15 per cent of the subjects treated, reduced in another 50 per cent and unchanged in 35 per cent. Heterosexual feeling is not significantly changed.

REFERENCES

1. Freund, K. (1963). A laboratory method for diagnosing predominance of homo- or hetero-erotic interest in the male. *Behav. Res. Ther.* **1**, 85-93.
2. Freund, K., Sedlacek, F. & Knob, K. (1965). A simple transducer for mechanical plethysmography of the male genital. *J. exp. Analysis Behav.* **8**, 169-70.

SEMINAR TWO : **PAPER TWO**

Aversion Therapy of a Sexual Deviation

Dr. S. H. Lovibond

The case to be presented is that of a fifteen-year-old boy referred by the Psychology Branch of the Social Welfaer Department for possible behaviour therapy.

About eight months previously the boy had been brought before the courts after a female horse had been found in a very distressed condition with stones and sticks inserted into her vagina. The boy admitted having interfered with the animal, and was released on bond. Later, following a similar offence, he was remanded to a psychiatric hospital for investigation and possible treatment.

The boy was examined by several psychiatrists, but no specific treatment had been undertaken when he absconded and was later found in the vicinity of a racecourse. He was taken back, but shortly afterwards absconded again. This time he managed to find a mare and interfere with her before being apprehended.

At this stage, the superintendent of the psychiatric hospital refused to have the boy back and he was placed in a remand home. As a desperate last move, I was asked if I felt I could do anything for the boy to avoid his incarceration in a juvenile prison. I agreed to see the boy and to look into the possibility of some form of behaviour therapy.

I found that the boy had lived with his stepfather and grandmother on their orchard and market garden property in a rather remote area about twelve miles from Adelaide. The boy's stepmother had been burned to death in a bushfire when he was about five years old, but other than that there appeared to be nothing unusual in his background. The lad was of low intelligence and was extraordinarily uncommunicative. Consequently I failed completely to get any worth-while information about the origins of the boy's somewhat unusual behaviour in relation to horses. He denied that he had obtained any sort of pleasure or excitement from his series of acts, and he referred to these in an oddly detached manner as "the first offence", "the second offence" and so on.

There was no suggestion of any other form of behaviour disorder, and I decided to accept the boy for behaviour therapy.

Before undertaking treatment it would have been valuable to have had an objective measure of the strength of the boy's sexual arousal in the presence of female horses. The penile plethysmograph would have been ideal for the purpose, but the necessary equipment was not available. I decided instead to use the galvanic skin reflex as a measure of the non-specific arousal value of horses compared with neutral and heterosexual stimuli. Pictures of mares, nude females and outdoor scenes were presented to the lad in a randomized sequence. Galvanic skin responses were significantly higher to both the nude females and the female horses than to the neutral scenes.

The general form of therapy

The next problem was to decide on the most suitable form of behaviour therapy. Since the undesirable behaviour was an approach response which presumably was being positively reinforced, a form of aversion therapy seemed most appropriate.

Type of aversive reinforcement

Next it was necessary to decide on the type of aversive stimulus to be used. Eysenck, Rachman and others have emphasized the advantages of electrical aversive stimuli over drugs such as apomorphine. The chief advantage is the greater controllability of electric shock. In particular, the duration of the US and the inter-stimulus interval, i.e. the interval between CS and US onset, are much more under control.

There is a good deal of evidence to suggest that these time relations are not nearly as important in the passive avoidance or punishment situation, as in classical aversive conditioning. There were, however, other reasons for preferring electric shock. These reasons will become apparent in a moment.

The stimuli to be made aversive

The next decision concerned the stimuli to be made aversive. Broadly, there was a choice of three types of stimuli — imaginal stimuli, visual stimuli provided by pictures, or, finally, stimulation arising from the actual context of the behaviour to be eliminated. Imaginal and pictorial stimuli have the advantage of permitting treatment to take place in the laboratory, and are often used when treatment in the actual situation is impracticable.

Although there is evidence that there is usually considerable generalization from imaginal and pictorial stimuli to the real life situation, there are obvious advantages to be gained by getting as close to the criterion situation as possible. In the present case such a procedure seemed to present no special difficulties and it was decided to negatively reinforce approaches to real mares. Since such a programme required a portable method of administering the aversive reinforcement, the use of electric shock was virtually mandatory.

ESCAPE VERSUS NON-ESCAPE CONDITIONING

At this stage it was necessary to select the specific form of aversive conditioning to be used: classical or instrumental. Briefly, the difference has to do with whether the aversive stimulus is applied for a fixed period of time, or whether it is kept on until some designated response occurs. In the latter case the designated response provides escape from the aversive stimulus. Recently there has been a tendency to favour escape conditioning in aversion therapy. For example, in the aversion therapy of alcoholism, the shock is turned on when the subject drinks alcohol, and he escapes from shock by spitting the alcohol out.

My own experimental work has led me to conclude that the provision of escape is of little consequence in the suppression of undesired behaviour, and it has the serious disadvantage of initially limiting the intensity of the aversive stimulus that can be used.

The rule, which it seems to me can be derived from a number of lines of evidence, is to present aversive stimuli of high intensity if permanent suppression of behaviour is desired.

My own work also suggests that it is important not to use a shock of very short duration. On these grounds, it was decided to use an intense shock with a fixed duration of some two seconds.

THE SCHEDULE OF REINFORCEMENT

There is evidence that the greater the unpredictability of the aversive stimulation the more permanent the response suppression is likely to be. One way of increasing unpredictability is to use an intermittent reinforcement schedule. That is to say, the response is allowed to occur without the aversive reinforcement on some occasions selected at random. In the present instance I obviously could not allow the undesired behaviour to occur in its entirety, so that intermittent reinforcement was impracticable. I decided, therefore, to increase the unpredictability of the aversive event by varying the time of shock onset after the start of the approach response.

THE CONDUCT OF TREATMENT

At this point I explained to the boy what I proposed to do. I told him that if he agreed after I'd explained what was involved, I would take him out to a secluded spot in the country. I would obtain a female horse which would be tied to a nearby tree. I would then require him to approach the horse with a stick in hand from a distance of 30–40 feet. He would have shock electrodes attached to his fingers, and, at a certain point in the approach to the horse, he would receive a rather severe electric shock. I explained that the shock would be quite intense. It would be something like the shock from a car spark plug but somewhat stronger. I emphasized that I could not guarantee to eliminate the boy's impulse to interfere with animals, nor was I able to guarantee that he would be released after completing the course of therapy. Nevertheless, I felt there was a good chance of a successful outcome. No doubt because he understood that the alternative was certain incarceration, the boy willingly gave his consent to the carrying out of the programme. The consent of the boy's stepfather was also forthcoming.

After receiving an explanation of the programme and an assurance that no harm would come to the animals, the proprietor of a riding school agreed to make a number of mares available.

On the first day, shock electrodes in circuit with an inductorium were attached to the first and third fingers of the boy's left hand. The hand was covered by a glove. Three trials were given about five minutes apart. At different points in the approach to the horse, the shock was turned on at high intensity and kept on for two seconds. For the second treatment session one week later, a different mare was obtained, and the treatment was carried out in a different locality. This time, after only one trial, the boy utterly refused to go near the horse again. At this stage there was no doubt about the amount of anxiety that was being generated in the situation. The boy broke out into a sweat and kicked at the ground. He was very agitated and protested that he "couldn't do it". I was now in something of a quandary. There had been only four reinforcements, and ordinarily this number would not be regarded as sufficient to ensure a high degree of resistance to extinction. If I continued to put pressure on the boy to make the approach response, suppression of the response might be further reinforced by the anxiety generated in the situation, despite the absence of further shocks. In other words secondary reinforcement might further strengthen the required learning. On the other hand, continued exposure to the situation without further shocks might tend to produce extinction of the conditioned anxiety, thus weakening response suppression. Unfortunately, the literature on passive avoidance learning, or punishment, offered no guidance. As a compromise, I decided to bring the boy back on two further occasions, and to attempt to get him to make further approaches to the horse.

The third and fourth treatment sessions were also a week apart, with different mares, and in different localities. At the start of the third session the shock electrodes were fitted and the boy was urged to approach the mare with a stick. He was told that more shocks were necessary in order to complete the cure. Pressure was kept on for two minutes, during which time there was considerable agitation, but no approach response. The boy was then allowed to rest for five minutes with the electrodes off, well away from the mare. Two further two minute trials were given with a five minute rest interval. As before no approach response could be obtained.

The final session one week later was a repeat of the third session. Again on each of three trials there was obvious anxiety, and refusal or inability to make the approach response. There were no obvious signs that anxiety in the situation had in any way decreased. If anything the anxiety seemed to have increased.

At the conclusion of the third trial, the electrodes were removed and the boy was asked to approach the horse and pat it. Again there was agitation and refusal to approach the horse. When it was suggested to him that he could not possibly be shocked now, as the electrodes were off, he replied, "I don't trust that thing." Later he said with some feeling, "I never want to see a horse again."

A week later the boy was given a repeat of the GSR test. The only change was a somewhat higher response to the pictures of horses, presumably an anxiety reaction.

Subsequently the boy was placed on probation and allowed to return home. In the meantime he had left school and his grandmother had died. This meant that now there was only the boy's stepfather in the house. The stepfather worked very long hours, and as the boy was not working, he was left alone in the house for long periods. As there were horses within half a mile of the house, the stage seemed set for a relapse. The boy remained in these unfavourable circumstances for some months and then began to work with his father.

It is now fourteen months since treatment was completed, and relapse has not occurred.

At the end of six months the boy was interviewed and tested by a psychologist of the Social Welfare Department. The boy said he no longer had any desire to approach horses, and insisted that he had been cured by the treatment. This was the first time that he had admitted ever having had an impulse to approach horses — it had been something that "just happened".

Although in a single case one can never be certain that a favourable outcome is attributable to the therapeutic programme, in the present case such an interpretation does not lack plausibility.

DISCUSSION

Professor Hammer: I would like to know what the boy thinks about you?

Dr. Lovibond: Well, interestingly enough, from what he said to the staff psychologists, though he did not quite express it in these terms, he seemed to be quite grateful to me. He never expressed this to me, and indeed he never has admitted to me ever having had these impulses in the first place. But to the psychologist he did express a positive feeling towards me.

—————: Would Dr. Lovibond like to express an opinion about the relative value of the use of shock in the situation compared with the ordinary forms of punishment as, say, a stockwhip or a cane?

Dr. Lovibond: I have no doubt that if you could somehow arrange it so that you could follow the boy around without his knowing you were there, and ensure that during the course of his approach response he was hit with a stockwhip, then this would produce the same effect. But if you took him after his apprehension, and flogged him a day later, then you would produce no effect whatsoever. In other words, the punishment in this sense is only effective if it closely and consistently follows the response to be treated.

Dr. Nurcombe: What grounds are there for assuming there was no psychosis?

Dr. Lovibond: None, I suppose, just a hunch again. I am convinced, myself, that psychotic forms of disorder are made of a different kind of stuff and not to be compared with the non-psychotic forms of behaviour disorder; and despite the lack of concrete evidence that there are specific biochemical factors involved in schizophrenia for example, I personally remain convinced that at some stage or other we will find that the critical causal agent is something of this nature. So I tend to think of psychotic disturbances as being entirely different. As a consequence, I would have backed away from this case on no other grounds than that.

Dr. McConaghy: Do you know what form of treatment the boy had had before you saw him?

Dr. Lovibond: I was a little bit disappointed because I was not able to turn up evidence that he had had twelve months' psychotherapy or play therapy or something of this sort. Most cases I have been called on to deal with do have this sort of background. Often the psychologist at the child guidance clinic rings me up and says he has a child, for example, with symptoms of urgency and frequency as well as being nocturnally enuretic, and could I do something about it? I ask what has been done, and find he has been on play therapy for twelve months, and nothing seems to have happened. Well, in this case it was not so. Apparently in the psychiatric hospital they had not got around to doing anything about him. I think that they did not quite know how to proceed, but I am not sure. Anyway there was no specific treatment, to my knowledge.

Mrs. Dorothy Rowe: How long did the whole treatment take?

Dr. Lovibond: I think the whole thing from when I saw him to when he was released would have been about six weeks. During this time he was retained in a remand home, where, of course, he was subjected to all sorts of influences over which I had no control. The fact that I only wanted the boy for four sessions seemed to worry the people at the Social Welfare Department, who felt that they could not persuade the authorities that anything useful could be done for the boy in such a short time.

SEMINAR TWO : PAPER THREE

The Treatment of Tics by Massed Practice

Professor A. J. Yates

About ten years ago, I published a paper on the application of learning theory to the treatment of tics[1] in which I conceptualized the tic, theoretically, as a drive-reducing conditioned avoidance response, originally generated in a highly traumatic situation. By the usual learning processes of generalization, conceptualization, and so on, it becomes attached to a wide variety of stimuli. In terms of Hull's theoretical constructs, which were still quite popular at that time — though they seem to have fallen into some disrepute since — we derived a method of treatment which was based on Hull's very well-known equation, viz.:

$$_{s}\bar{E}_{R} = (_{s}H_{R} \times D) - (I_{R} + _{s}I_{R})$$

For our purposes, we need not worry about subsequent modifications of this equation. The capacity to perform the tic was regarded as being a function of the excitatory part of the equation, i.e. $_{s}H_{R}$ is the actual strength of the tic which has been built up through repeated evocation. Its strength of evocation on any given occasion would be a function not only of its actual habit strength, but also of the drive level of the patient, just as we perform a skilled response more strongly in a state of high drive than in a state of low drive. We proposed to make use of the inhibitory part of Hull's equation by getting the patient to indulge in what is called "massed practice", that is, the voluntary evocation of the tic by the patient with a very short time interval between each successive evocation.

Under these conditions, we argued, the patient would build up reactive inhibition (I_{R}) to the point at which he would be forced to rest, i.e. not perform the tic. During this rest period, reactive inhibition would decline or dissipate as a function of time, and since reactive inhibition is an aversive form of stimulation, its dissipation over time would be rewarding. We argued that what would be rewarding in this situation would be the response of not performing the tic. Since you cannot both perform and not perform the same response simultaneously, if we could build up increments of $_sI_R$ (the negative habit) by accumulating reactive inhibition and allowing it to dissipate, we should eventually build up an incompatible habit which would act against the positive habit $_sH_R$, and if we could make $_sI_R$ strong enough, then the patient would simply not be able to perform the tic any further.

This was in line with the notion that motor habits, at least, once they are acquired cannot be destroyed in the sense that you can cut off an arm. They can only be replaced by some alternative incompatible response, and this was our aim. This argument, or rationale, was based on a great deal of work with animals. In humans, at that time, we had no idea under what conditions we could build up $_sI_R$ optimally. Thus we embarked on what was essentially a long-term experiment — it was explained to the patient that it was an experiment, and not a form of treatment — in which we attempted to discover the optimal conditions for building up the negative habit, $_sI_R$.

The experiment with this patient lasted some nine months, and at the end of that time we found that the patient was almost unable to perform three of the four tics which we had attempted to eliminate. One of our problems at that time, of course, was to generalize the negative habit outside the laboratory — a problem which I mentioned this morning — and one on which, at that time, we did not do very much work. Clearly one way of generalizing the negative habit would be to get the patient to do massed practice in the kind of situations in which the tic was evoked. Socially, of course, it might be very undesirable for the patient to perform these responses voluntarily in various public places. The alternative, which we did not succeed in carrying out, was to generalize the habit not to places, but to people, and particularly to critical people. So one further development of this approach would have been to get the patient to practise the tics in situations which involved people who became increasingly critical of the patient — the kind of situation which she found in real life. She did claim that there was some considerable generalization to real life, but this was essentially anecdotal evidence.

However, in terms of a possible technique, with the suggested modifications for future cases, it did look to some people as though we might here have a standard method of treatment. The point I made this morning is that there are no standard methods of treatment, and one cannot simply go on to the next patient and assume that this method will work as it did for the first patient. We simply do not have enough theoretical and practical knowledge at this stage. Whereas at first we had started off with very short periods of massed practice, of the order of one minute or so, at the end of our series of experiments, our conclusion on the basis of these experiments was that what we should really do was to utilize very prolonged periods of massed practice, up to five or six or more hours in duration, followed by very prolonged periods of rest of the order of two to three weeks. This might sound a somewhat difficult thing for the patient to do, and rather painful and unpleasant, but in fact you should remember that under these conditions of prolonged massed practice, the patient spends the vast majority of the five or six hours doing nothing, because she is unable after the first fifteen minutes or so to perform the tic at all. The fact that she is not performing the tic, of course, is part of the treatment, and therefore not to be looked down on from the point of view of the experiment. However we did not, unfortunately, carry out all of these further steps which would have been highly desirable.

Subsequently a colleague of mine, Gwynne Jones,[2] whose name is very well known in this area, carried this technique further with various modifications, but not the kind I have discussed as highly desirable, and he was almost as surprised as I was to find that the status the patient had reached when I had finished the experiment with her was maintained when she transferred over to him. In fact, throughout this experiment, I must confess that whenever the patient was given any prolonged rest, I fully expected that when she came back the tics would have been restored to their former glory.

Similarly a man called Rafi[3] carried out subsequently an experiment using massed practice, and with some qualifications repeated my findings, as did Walton.[4] So it would appear at this stage that we had a fairly standard method at least to start off with, and could go on from there. However, what I want to mention this afternoon, without going into too much detail, is a very recent experiment in which not only did the workers fail to obtain these results, but they found that the tics became very considerably worse under conditions of massed practice. This was a study by Feldman and Werry[5] in which they took a thirteen and a half year old boy with multiple tics on the face, neck and head. Of these multiple tics they chose two for treatment, viz. a rather complicated head-jerk, and an eye-blink, one of the tics which my patient had. Their study, in many respects, was a considerable improvement on my own; for example, they measured the baseline rate of each of the tics before each experimental session — that is, the baseline involuntary rate of tics — and, further, they did what I should have done but did not think of doing, and retained one of the two tics they were considering as an untreated control. This in fact is what I meant this morning when I was talking about the internal validation of behaviour therapy.

They also measured both the voluntary rate of the tics and the involuntary rate of the tics, although as far as I can recall they did not measure the involuntary rate outside the experimental situation. What they found was that during the experimental periods of massed practice, not only did the involuntary tics increase very dramatically in frequency, but the patient was able to increase the voluntary rate of tics very dramatically as well. This was even worse in a way than simply failing to get any change. They actually got a worsening of the situation under these conditions.

Now this, I think, is an almost classic instance of the kind of problem which the behaviour therapist must face up to. It is simply not good enough to say, as, in effect, Feldman and Werry virtually did say, "Here we have a technique which we have applied to an individual patient; it has not worked, full stop. Hard luck on the patient, but that's that."

They did suggest two possible theoretical explanations for these findings, but they did not do any further experimentation on the patient. Their first explanation was that the habit strength of the tic was not maximized at the beginning of treatment — one of the assumptions that I had made — and that therefore practice in performing the tic increased the strength of the tic. This certainly could happen if the tic was not maximized. However they reject this as a possible explanation, and in my view quite rightly, on various grounds. The second explanation, which they accept, is that the experimental procedure itself, in this particular instance at least, increased drive strength and thereby increased the excitatory potential as in the above equation. Thus any effects of massed practice were overshadowed.

I do not know whether their second explanation is correct or not, but clearly what they should have done was to attempt to vary drive levels of the patient; because if their theory is correct, then by the use of drugs or other means they should be able to vary the strength of the patient's drive and hence show systematic changes in the capacity to perform the tic.

More generally, the result raises some interesting questions, because here we have a clear-cut instance where the original method has been satisfactorily replicated by three different workers in widely different situations all using the same technique, and then along comes someone who, as far as I can judge, used essentially the same technique — though there are certainly variations, for example, in the amount of massed practice and so on — and finds not merely negative results, but apparently what one might reasonably call quite opposite results. The patient apparently became much worse, so much worse that he did not want to continue with the experiment.

What should we do in a situation like this? Should we just give the patient away and say "I'm sorry, but that's the end of it", or do we now really get down to business and start looking at these experiments in great detail? If behaviour is lawful, and if we can arrive, ultimately, at rational explanations for behaviour, then clearly there must be a rational explanation for these conflicting results, particularly as on one side we have four studies which are in agreement and on the other we have one study which is in total disagreement. There must be a rational explanation.

This to me is an illustration of precisely what I mean by behaviour therapy. In my view the next step must be further experimentation — with this individual preferably, but otherwise with other individuals — in an attempt to resolve the differences which we have found. The critical point, in my view, is that whether or not these methods succeed in alleviating the patient's disorder, careful examination and further experimentation along these lines will lead to an increase in knowledge which ultimately will benefit future patients, and therefore I think would be fully justified.

REFERENCES

1. Yates, A.J. (1958). The application of learning theory to the treatment of tics. *J. abnorm. soc. Psychol.* **56**, 175-82.
2. Jones, H.G. (1960). Continuation of Yates' treatment of a tiqueur. In *Behaviour therapy and the neuroses* (ed. H.J. Eysenck), pp. 250-58. Oxford: Pergamon.
3. Rafi, A.A. (1962). Learning theory and the treatment of tics. *J. psychosom. Res.* **6**, 71-76.
4. Walton, D. (1961). Experimental psychology and the treatment of a tiqueur. *J. Child Psychol. Psychiat.* **2**, 148-55.
5. Feldman, R.B. & Werry, J.S. (1966). An unsuccessful attempt to treat a tiqueur by massed practice. *Behav. Res. Ther.* **4**, 111-17.

DISCUSSION

Mr. Whitford: In these studies, how much information is available about the subjects in terms of biographical and personality data?

Professor Yates: I'm not sure about the other studies, but in my own case we had measures of neuroticism, introversion-extraversion and intelligence. However, we didn't make any use of them. We might well have done so, of course, because one of the strongest points that Eysenck has made is the interaction between learning theory and personality, particularly in relation to drugs and their effects on conditioning. The question is, what information along those lines is relevant to the particular treatment under discussion? I think the answer to that question is that we don't really know. This is one of the major areas of research in which we are grossly deficient at the present time. This is another reason why I think it is misleading to ask at this stage, "Does behaviour therapy work?". After a mere ten years, it doesn't seem to me that one can expect any answer to this question. This is the danger as I see it. People would say, "Here is the patient, here is the technique, it works or it doesn't." That, I think, would be the death of behaviour therapy.

Dr. Lovibond: You said that you didn't actually take measures of the operant level; presumably you didn't notice any increase here?

Professor Yates: You mean in real life?

Dr. Lovibond: Yes.

Professor Yates: Well, we had the patient, more for interest than anything else, keep a very detailed record of her attitudes towards what was being done and so on, and two things did strike us, although this is quite anecdotal. Firstly, she said that people no longer asked her what was the matter with her when she went into a crowded room. People no longer asked her whether she had a cold, for instance. (She had a nasal tic and also a throat-clearing tic.) Secondly, and more strikingly, was an event which puzzled me for a while, until I realized what the likely explanation was. After about three or four months of this experiment, she came up to me and said, "I've discovered how I can stop the tic from occurring when I want it to. For example, when I go into a room to be interviewed by somebody

69

I don't know, all I have to do is to say to myself, 'stop it' and the tic goes away for about fifteen minutes." This puzzled me for a while, because I couldn't see any connection between that and the massed practice rationale, until I realized that by this time the patient had performed something like 2,000 separate one-minute periods of massed practice, at the end of each of which I had said, "Stop", and the patient had stopped. It seems that here is an instance of a quite simple associative mechanism, where the association of the word "stop" with actually stopping the performance of the tic, over this long period of time, had resulted in the saying of the word actually inhibiting the performance of the tic for a certain period of time.

Mr. R. Hinkler: I was treating a patient using a procedure very similar to the one you mentioned. This patient had a tremor when playing the violin. After some months of massed practice, there was a decline as measured by tape-recordings and so on in the occurrence of the tremor, and the patient reported exactly that same phrase: "When I feel the tremor coming I can stop it, but I have to use the word, 'Stop'." To me it's still a question as to why the patient can do this. I thought it might be something to do with kinaesthetic control.

Professor Yates: Yes, I wouldn't want to suggest that verbal feedback is the only kind of stimulus which can inhibit behaviour; I think we haven't even begun to touch the important subject of internal, kinaesthetic and sensory feedback which the Russians are working on so much. I think this is one of the most important areas which has been neglected almost completely in the West; although there are one or two workers, such as Hefferline,[1] who have demonstrated very dramatically the extent to which subjects can respond to extremely minute sensory feedback changes without even being aware that they are doing so. This is an area which we haven't begun to touch as yet.

REFERENCES

1. Hefferline, R.F. (1958). The role of proprioception in the control of behaviour. *Trans. N.Y. Acad. Sci.* **20**, 739-64.

RECAPITULATION: SUMMARY OF POINTS COVERED IN SEMINARS ONE AND TWO

RECAPITULATION:

Summary of Points Covered in Seminars One and Two

Professor A. G. Hammer

I certainly do not propose to try to recapitulate all of the important points that have been covered by the main speakers today.

This afternoon I think we have had three very good illustrations of the variety and some of the limitations of behaviour therapy. It would have been impossible to present these cases before the earlier theoretical discussion, yet in a way I can well imagine that discussion will be more concerned with this concrete clinical material. What has been shown is that the behaviour therapy techniques produce certain results. Two or three instances do not prove anything, but if these are typical examples they show that these techniques of doing things to people are producing results. Whether they are therapeutic or not might be something for you to consider. There is also a hint that they are producing these results only in certain circumstances or with certain sorts of cases. I am not sure how to refer to these limitations. I do not know whether the cases are monosymptomatic cases, or cases in which one symptom is being treated at a time, whether they are simple or complex. One notion that enters my mind is that they are ones in which the behaviour contingencies are somehow within, or brought within, the control of the therapist. It is not so much a matter of simplicity as a matter of a situation in which the psychologist is able to do something about it, where the consequences of the behaviour are in some sense within the control of the therapist. I think Dr. Lovibond gave us a very good example of how, when this is not the case, it is necessary in fact experimentally to make it so. This was the essence of his answer to the question asked by Mr. Whitford. However, this might also be a matter which you would like to follow up.

When Dr. McConaghy was talking, it was quite clear he was giving an account of an experimental procedure which was causing something to happen. Were the changes the sorts of things we call therapy, even in the narrower sense? Were these people becoming non-homosexual? Consider Dr. Lovibond's case. Was the boy acquiring a "horse phobia"? That is important; maybe Dr. Lovibond's decision that a horse phobia is better than the original compulsion is sound, but was there no other way to cure? Did Dr. Lovibond think it was just that? Further, if the horse phobia was explained in terms of ordinary conditioning, why also was not there a Lovibond phobia? This has not been explained. We have only heard about contiguity, reinforcement patterns, and so on. You can rationalize the facts another way. You can begin to talk in psychoanalytic terms about identification with the aggressor — that is, to defend himself from anxiety generated by Dr. Lovibond's punitive aggression the patient takes in Dr. Lovibond's attitude to horses.

I want to ask you also to consider whether there are not differences between cases where the responses seem to be somewhat under voluntary control and those where they are not. What is the role of the conditioned reflex in behaviour generally? That is the basic theoretical question. In a sense it is impossible to take up an issue like that at a meeting such as this, but behind all the discussion, it seems to be lurking. Let me illustrate with two cases. There is one reported fairly recently where a boy is taught to desist from theft — and he was a genuine compulsive thief — by the psychologist's building up a reinforcement relationship between the boy and a mothering type figure in the orphanage. This the boy did really appreciate, enjoying this sort of reinforcement for the first time. Then, after that relationship was established, deprivation of the reinforcement became the consequence of any particular act of theft. There followed an extraordinary reduction. However, it seems to me that this is ordinary education or re-education, that this is the sort of thing that wise parents do, and that this boy was not operating as a "conditioned-reflex-acquiring machine" at all. He had learnt, by virtue of the way in which he was being dealt with, that it paid better not to thieve and that he could get his rewards in another way.

Compare this with a different application of the same sort of principle. I had a patient who was an enormous burper — she burped and burped. Of course, she was a compulsive air-swallower. We tried all sorts of treatment — non-directive therapy, modified psychoanalytic therapy and so on, and got nowhere. Then we set up a schedule of reward withholding. We discovered that the patient liked listening to radio serials. We tape recorded a variety of relatively simple stories. She sat in a room, listening to these stories. We had a little air thing around her neck, and every time she swallowed the tape recorder went off, and the story was interrupted for one or two minutes. She became very much better indeed. She had no idea of what was happening and still does not know. This case seems to me to be somewhat nearer to the real conditioning model.

Now what was happening in Lovibond's case? Lovibond has come out and said (and I like his view, I think I agree with almost everything he said) that his account is not theoretically orientated. This is empirical work; it has a relatively low level of generalization. We know — Thorndike said this a long time ago — that when things pay off, people do them again, and when they do not pay off they give them away. So we try to control, with care for the time-relations and the like, the rewards and punishments. But I think we have to go further and ask why.

Professor Yates's emphasis has been on the study of the individual case. Most of us here agree with him. But, as I said to him, he wants to talk about one topic, and others of us think that something else is the topic. There is no real disagreement here amongst us; there are some disagreements, but no basic ones, except perhaps this, that he wants to use the term "behaviour therapy" to refer to the careful, objective, scientific controlled study of the individual case, while some of us feel that although that sort of thing is worth a special name, "behaviour therapy" refers to something else. It refers to the application of a variety of objective-type psychological principles especially based on conditioned reflex psychology to behaviour disorders. I agree with Yates that the psychologist has to be like a detective, a person who is applying the hypothetico-deductive method to the individual case, and not too often descending to mere routine. I think he hasn't fully answered the question of just which premise in the hypothetico-deductive argument is under scrutiny. Is it the general principle or is it the minor premise? There are matters of scientific method here to be worked out. My agreement with him is general, I would want to go into further discussion of details. There is plenty of room for a whole seminar on the application of the hypothetico-deductive method to the individual case, which, incidentally, I think can be achieved independently of the objectivity of the method. The hypothetico-deductive method is applicable to the individual case within the psychoanalytic framework, which is a highly subjective one.

The speakers in this seminar were not talking about the same

75

thing. There is an area of overlap, because when Yates says that behaviour therapists are dealing with independent variables, he thinks of $_sH_R$ or habit strength. Now I would be willing to talk of things like intentions, a word which has meaning even without definition. When one says to a young man "what are your intentions", everyone knows what is meant. I would not reject such subjective notions in applying the hypothetico-deductive method.

Back to Lovibond. I am still not satisfied that Lovibond does really — although he said he does — make a clear distinction between ordinary learning and the acquisition of psychopathological structures. I am not sure that the ordinary fears, as of snakes, are any more than ordinary fears. I am not sure that they are phobic. It seems to me that there is something qualitatively different in that a person with a phobia is not merely ready to go away when a snake comes along, but spends all his life hoping he will never come into contact with a snake even though it is most unlikely that he will. It is this sort of thing that made Freud say "this bloke who looks as if he is afraid of a snake must really be afraid of something he wants to get close to". It still remains to be seen whether there is not a difference between many of the fears that have been treated by behaviour therapy methods and the genuine phobias of the psychoanalysts.

Professor Whitlock issued a very useful challenge to behaviour therapists who were speaking today. He reminded us that people are treated and not symptoms. I think we are entitled to ask, without being sentimental, just how far symptoms are a part of the person. Lovibond said that some evidence shows that enuresis is not a very big part of the person. If a person has a wart on his finger, the doctor can chop the wart off without worrying too much about the whole person. If on the other hand, the person's illness is a cancer riddling the whole of the body, the complications are different in that the whole of the person has to be dealt with.

Professor Whitlock also raised the ethical question, which I think is tremendously important, and again a whole seminar weekend could be devoted to this. There are a number of questions that he was raising. I think one was: what are the side effects? We do not want to do something to a person if we produce some other harmful effects or if for instance we cause pain so great that it is not justified by the result. Now we must specify clearly that this is what is meant, if that is what is meant.

Another possible meaning is that we do not like methods involving punishing. Punishment seems to be unethical. On this one I shall stick my neck out. This is a woolly-minded, soft attitude, any scientist worth his salt is simply a determinist who says that the consequences of behaviour in the long run are predictable. The task is to discover what are the consequences of doing X and then, on some other grounds which are not psychological, to decide whether those consequences are wanted or not. If these are the consequences you want, then you will do it. If you do not do it, then there is an equally predictable result. While some people might have thought that Lovibond's methods were pretty rough, if he had not used them there was a good chance that the boy would be still going round making life pretty hard for mares, or alternatively having a pretty unhappy time in some sort of institution. Frankly, as a determinist, I think the real issue here is not whether one likes punishment or not — I do not like hurting people either — but what the consequences are. I suggest there were two possible sorts of consequence:

1. That punishment may actually reduce the strength of the pathological $_sH_R$ bond. In that case, there seems to me not the slightest case against the use of the rough techniques.

2. That punishment does not reduce the strength of the $_sH_R$ bond, but stacks up a strong fear against it. I do not know whether that is very good. I do not think I would regard it as very successful to give a boy a phobia of horses as a way of preventing him from doing what this boy was doing. There must be some better way in the long run, though this might be useful temporarily.

SEMINAR THREE: PSYCHOTHERAPY AND BEHAVIOUR THERAPY COMPARED

SEMINAR THREE : PAPER ONE

Dr. B. Nurcombe

When this conference was being organized I was hopeful that my own participation would be passive and receptive. Since this has not proven the case I should like to offer the following reflections. These can be regarded as the comments of an eclectic psychiatrist, analytically oriented in training and practice, but sympathetic to innovation.

To begin with, four short case histories. I leave the audience to draw whatever conclusions they will from these anecdotes.

The first psychiatric patient I ever treated was a dependent young man unable to walk because of hysterical paralysis of the legs. He had been transferred to the psychiatric ward after languishing for months in a plaster cast in the orthopaedic ward. By this time he was heartily sick of the physical and economic inconvenience and ripe for cure. He quickly formed a strong positive and dependent transference to the eager young resident, and after an exploration of the traumatic circumstances surrounding the onset of the symptom it required only strong suggestion to mobilize him. Seeking to hasten the dramatic cure I instituted a regime of regular morning skipping. Unfortunately, while being encouraged by an enthusiastic nurse, the patient sprained his ankle and was returned temporarily to bed.

The second case is a physically and intellectually impressive young man who presented with writer's cramp in the second year of his university course. This symptom had developed just before his first year examinations which he had completed with difficulty. The dynamics of the condition were not difficult to elucidate. The patient had for long been involved in a competitive oedipal struggle with a powerful father whose all-round excellence served

81

as a goal to be surpassed. At secondary school the patient had been a champion athlete notable for his "killer instinct", and the dux of his class as well. When he found that the competition of his university colleagues was less easy to overcome, the symptom developed. In short he feared not failure but not doing supremely well. By this stage, however, time was running out as the second year examinations were imminent. After he had gained a limited insight, complete symptomatic recovery was attained by the use of suggestion and practice under hypnosis. He sat for his examination and wrote perfectly. Unfortunately he omitted to notice on a vital paper the clearly marked instructions to attempt two compulsory questions. Thus he chose failure by mischance over mediocre performance by commitment.

The third patient was brought to see me after he had been paralysed by anxiety in the examination room. He expressed a terror of the examination situation and found himself quite unable to think or write. The roots of his neurosis did not become apparent until some time afterwards. He had been rejected by a disturbed and egocentric mother during a childhood which was marred by a chronic, painful and immobilizing illness. His only support was his father, a mediocre man who had attempted to compensate through his son by impressing on him the need to be notable and successful. This became the boy's imperative obligation if he wished to retain the love of his parent. His but moderate ability made the goal unattainable in university and he was faced clearly with what he most urgently feared in fantasy: failure, rejection, and abandonment. There was no time, however, for exploration as the supplementary examinations were approaching. Under hypnosis he was encouraged to relax, to enter the phobic situation in imagination, with strong suggestion as to his capacity for facing it. When the time came he sat for all papers without incident. Unfortunately he failed since he had been unable to study effectively over the summer vacation. He chose to fail by default rather than fall short after commitment.

The nearest approach to a monosymptomatic illness that I have seen recently was presented by a young man with the following complaint. He was prone to blush vividly and conspicuously when others made personal remarks about him. The condition had commenced some time before when his sister teased him about a girl friend, in front of his prudish and scrupulous mother. Matters had got to the point where he was avoiding tutorials through fear that he would blush if the lecturer directed a question at him. Apart from this he seemed a well-adjusted man, with an excellent scholastic and sporting record, and capable of enjoying social intercourse to the full. There was some evidence of repressed conflict in the area of exhibitionism; he carried the Australian abhorrence of bragging to an extreme, yet was privately delighted to excel before a crowd in spectacular individual combat sports. Despite this he did not seem a highly neurotic person. In view of the fact that he could attend only intermittently it was thought practicable to adapt one technique from behaviour therapy. He was instructed to have his sister make personal remarks to him and to practise blushing. He was encouraged also to attend tutorials and when he felt a blush occurring to relax, welcome, and exhibit it. No exploratory work at all was done. His co-operation was obtained in carrying out this seemingly nonsensical advice. After about three months the symptom had abated considerably and he now felt he had it under control. He left for a southern city much heartened. He recently contacted me after twelve months, to say that he had been free of blushing for some time but it had recently returned and was as bad as ever.

As Marks and Gelder[1] point out, learning theories start with simple phenomena and try to build an explanation of complex behaviour from them; psychodynamic theory starts with complex behaviour and tries to analyse it into simpler components. Neither has yet given us a theory adequate to explain the origin and perpetuation of all forms of maladaptive neurotic behaviour.

A simple explanation in learning theory terms might be as follows. An individual in a double avoidance conflict (e.g. a man who dislikes his wife but fears leaving her) has his anxiety activated as he shifts from one distasteful response sequence to another. Escape from the field is prohibited by the circumstances. In such a situation it is physiologically likely that associations will be built up (conditioned) between the anxiety and chance events external or internal. The secondary learning of instrumental responses aimed at avoiding anxiety may then occur. Thus a conditioned phobia of enclosed spaces is avoided by not attending lectures or not entering lifts. Why does the maladaptive symptom persist? There are two possible explanations. Eysenck[2] for example considers that the avoidance response prevents opportunity for the extinction of an inappropriate primary conditioning through non-reinforcement. Others suggest that the maladaptive pattern persists because it is continually reinforced by the negative reward of relief from anxiety.

Psychoanalytic theory suggests that neurotic maladaptation originates in childhood. As a result of a traumatic or adverse environment the individual experiences disorganizing anxiety when he seeks to deploy primitive sexual or aggressive drives in an interpersonal context. To prevent the expression of these drives a complex structure of defences is built up. These distort later personality development, tending to cause a fixation of behaviour at an immature level. Pathological patterns of interpersonal behaviour then become transferred or generalized to other significant people in adulthood. These other people are then compelled to behave towards the individual in ways which perpetuate the pathology. The dependent person surrounds himself with protective friends; the paranoid man evokes suspiciousness or aggression, for example. Should a major precipitating trauma occur, such as the rupture of an important personal relationship, or if cumulative frustration resulting from the anachronistic behaviour itself becomes too much to tolerate, the defensive system breaks down and regression ensues back to the major fixation points. Drive tensions are then contained by the use of secondary defences in the form of symptoms.

The theory has therefore two facets. It emphasizes changes in internal structure arising from interpersonal experiences, together with the resultant pathological interpersonal behaviour stemming from this structural change. Not surprisingly, therapy emphasizes the interpersonal. A central consideration is the phenomenon of transference. The patient will tend to repeat with his therapist the anachronistic behaviour which has precipitated and perpetuated his difficulties. The transference is managed in different ways depending on the depth and goals of therapy. It may be fostered, interpreted, or diverted. Therapy provides a corrective emotional experience since, for the first time, a significant other person does not behave in the expected way but quietly and persistently asks the patient to examine the meaning of his behaviour. In all cases the therapist seeks an understanding of transference for to ignore it would be to overlook an important therapeutic and predictive phenomenon. Recent research in behaviour therapy suggests a growing interest in this problem.

The psychodynamic approach asserts that an attack on the symptom alone, without understanding or attempting to modify the interpersonal pathology of which the symptom is a reflection, is likely to be fruitless or even dangerous. Some behaviour therapists assert that the disturbed social behaviour is a result of the symptom and will disappear if the latter is removed. Others, including Wolpe[3] and Beech,[4] concede that a naïve view of symptomatology may be misleading and that careful enquiry into the interpersonal meaning of the symptom may unearth a more basic problem (such as the fear of authority) which may be dealt with by relearning techniques (such as encouraging "assertive" responses).

Despite the clangour of polemicists the two approaches have a good deal in common. Both involve a relationship between an expectant patient and a professional. Both have strong suggestive aspects, and both often deal at length with current sources of stress and repetitive patterns of behaviour. To some degree a common language is possible. Primary and secondary process have some relationship to classical and instrumental conditioning. Transference is clearly a form of stimulus or response generalization. Insight and "working-through" could be interpreted as the learning of alternative intermediate verbal responses reinforced by anxiety reduction in the therapeutic context. These verbal responses generalize to other situations and call forth more adaptive and flexible behaviour which is rewarded both positively and negatively. Psychotherapy does not deal solely with fantasy and recall; it relates the insight gained from these to the here-and-now. The patient is encouraged or aided to re-enter the phobic situation as in the treatment of school refusal.[5]

There are major points of difference, on the other hand. The techniques of free verbal association and interpretation of resistance and transference are philosophically distinct from those of reciprocal inhibition, negative practice or aversion. Psychotherapists assert that symptom removal without attention to unconscious conflict may lead to symptom substitution. The "cure" of alcoholism by aversive conditioning may be disappointing if the patient develops a suicidal depression thereafter. Behaviour therapists have tended to assert that symptom substitution rarely if ever occurs. It is likely in my opinion that both are correct.

Let us examine some particular instances. It is probable that many irrational fears arise from simple conditioning in a situation of trauma and conscious conflict; for example a fear of driving following a motor accident. The unconscious elements are minimal in this case. An explanation along learning theory lines is appropriate, and desensitization therapy will probably prove effective without symptom substitution. Other symptoms may be residual "habits" derived from an old unconscious conflict now inactive or "burnt-out". This appears to be the case in some forms of tic or enuresis, for example. Here, again, behaviour therapy is likely to be effective. Still other types of phobia, often associated with mixed obsessional symptoms, are surface manifestations of ongoing unconscious conflict; hence the failure of behaviour therapy alone to benefit the more severe forms of agoraphobia. In some forms of enuresis the symptom may be caused by a developmental lag in normal conditioning due probably to a variety of non-psychogenic factors. Conditioning techniques often prove strikingly successful in such cases. They are likely to fail, even to be consciously resisted, where the bedwetting serves to express unconscious drives and maintain the psychic economy of a conflicted individual.

The mutual antagonism between the two approaches has the flavour of an Eysenckian temperamental incompatibility. The "tough-minded" behaviour therapist knows what is best for his patient and applies a variety of directive techniques to that end. He is scornful of the interminability and equivocation of psychoanalysis and impatient with the imperfections of analytic theory and research. The psychotherapist desires his patient to discover his latent abilities as well as his limitations and go on to decide for himself what he wants to do. He is aware that the modification of engrained pathology is time-consuming and often incomplete. He sees the behaviour therapist as hiding behind mechanistic techniques to avoid a basic encounter with his patient as a human being. He is aware too of the potential political implications of certain forms of behaviour therapy applicable to people regarded as socially undesirable. In the polemics which have appeared in various publications it often appears that protagonists of both camps spend a great deal of time erecting and destroying straw-men. Eysenck for example utilizes very questionable figures to "prove" that psychotherapy does no more good than would be expected as a result of spontaneous recovery. Glover condemns behaviour therapy as a mere resurrection of nineteenth century suggestion therapy.

The eclectic therapist is a pragmatist. His working concepts are likely to be a patchwork. He may find that learning theory explains certain symptoms adequately. If he works with children he will regret the apparent absence of a developmental and interactional approach. Both theories explain certain phenomena fairly well. Neither explains all. Theories tend to develop in parallel, to decay when obsolete, to amalgamate where compatible. Total displacement of one by the other is improbable, although the time for a rapprochement is not yet. The practitioner must attempt to understand and help his patient now. He cannot wait for scientifically impeccable theories; consequently he will draw on diverse approaches. Art is long and Life is short, in the words of Hippocrates. Experiment is hazardous, experience often fallacious and judgment all too difficult.

REFERENCES
1. Marks, I.M. & Gelder, M.G. (1966). Common ground between behaviour therapy and psychodynamic methods. *Br. J. med. Psychol.* **39**, 11-23.
2. Eysenck, H.J. (1960). Modern learning theory. In *Behaviour therapy and the neuroses* (ed. H.J. Eysenck), p. 4. Oxford: Pergamon.
3. Wolpe, J. (1964). Behaviour therapy in complex neurotic states. *Br. J. Psychiat.* **110**, 28-34.
4. Beech, H.R. (1963). Some theoretical and technical difficulties in the application of behaviour therapy. *Bull. Br. psychol. Soc.* **16**, 25-33.
5. Patterson, G.R. & Brodsky, G. (1966). A behaviour modification programme for a child with multiple problem behaviours. *J. Child Psychol. Psychiat.* **7**, 277-95.

SEMINAR THREE : **PAPER TWO**

Dr. Elsie Harwood

I don't think, Mr. Chairman, that it was entirely my idea that I should come second on the programme, because we had indeed thought originally that this colloquium should take the form of two apologias for different kinds of therapy, and that I should compromise between the two, and therefore come last. There has been a sort of transference process between the two psychiatrists and myself. I fully understand now the problems that they have suffered, but both have found theirs to be soluble, and I am now faced with the problem of trying to compromise between two compromises, which I find myself rather unable to do. Therefore I am going to adopt a policy which they have already adopted, which is to state something in the way of a compromise, and to throw up a few comments which may be of use with respect to thinking or discussion.

First of all, I agree with Dr. McConaghy in his reference to the unfortunate term "behaviour therapy". If it had not been called behaviour therapy, I think perhaps that the other side might not have had as much need to be critical. And I well remember Eysenck, whose name occurs on books under this title so frequently, stating to an international conference only a couple of years ago, that it is unfortunate that the term "therapy" has been used, and that he would prefer the term "modification". It seems to me that the term "behaviour modification" better describes the symptom dismissal of which so much criticism has been made during the process of this conference.

Another comment that I would like to make before proceeding is that I feel that we have been a little lax, as we so often are in psychology, in the choice of terms. I have always been worried about people, practising what they call behaviour therapy, speaking glibly of people with phobias, who according to a stricter definition of the term, might be said to be suffering from some sort of fear, which to them was rather disturbing; but not in the sense in which we (of the old school) tend to use the term phobia — as something which is irrational or not explicable to the patient himself. I think Professor Whitlock brought up the problem of the people who are afraid of snakes (and like to think in terms of phobia). I believe that most people, if not all, who are really afraid of snakes, have been trained to be afraid of snakes, or have never met a snake; in either case they have some reason for treating the thing with respect. I would make a plea for a more careful definition of terms, in the interests of those who are quite rightly experimenting in this field of behaviour therapy.

I also want to say a word about the notion of causation, which has come up, of course, quite legitimately so many times. We find it rather difficult — at any rate those of us who have lived for so long with the procedures that were current — to get rid of the concept of cause. We know that the Rogerian methods of psychotherapy do not suggest that cause is important; in fact they frequently are able, at least in theory, to dismiss the idea of cause altogether. However, we have been accustomed to the Sherlock Holmes approach, regardless of the fact that there is no experimental evidence upon which the psychoanalyst can base his views of cause.

Moreover, I think that the word "cause", in relation to therapy in any form, should never be narrowly defined, because it must on some occasions and for some patients be expanded so as to connote an entire life-adjustment, due to upbringing, due to experience, and not simply an event in the life of the individual.

With regard to the question of symptom and anxiety, we have heard during the course of this conference a good deal of discussion on the removal of symptoms being followed by removal of anxiety. Clearly we don't know which takes precedence, a particular symptom or an anxiety which is associated with it. On the whole, it would seem that behaviour therapists are inclined to believe that the symptom causes the anxiety, and that if they remove the symptom the anxiety will go. But this is not certain, and possibly is not regarded as certain by all behaviour therapists. Any particular symptom may in fact result from anxiety. I think perhaps nail-biting might be regarded in some circumstances as almost invariably coming from anxiety and not creating anxiety in itself; it only creates anxiety when the parents, who are the primary behaviour therapists, get to work and try to stop it, and they generally do not stop it in as adequate a way as the psychological behaviour therapists would try to do.

We have to admit, I think, on whichever side of the fence we may sit, that there are some straightforward cases of people who have a behavioural symptom to which the processes of behaviour therapy may adequately be applied. I myself, coming from what might be described as the old school, and looking with a little caution, though not with distrust, at the new procedures, was trapped — and very appropriately — at Queen's University at Belfast where I went to conduct a postgraduate seminar at the clinical unit. I spoke with the utmost clarity to the man who sat with a hearing aid, as I thought, in front of me. He was a most vocal student who kept the seminar going for four and a half hours, and who, I thought, was doing a remarkably good job between the hearing aid and lip reading. When the seminar was over, Dr. Graham White asked me what I thought of the man who did all the talking. I said he was very keen, and also seemed to be able to hear very well. Dr. White's reply was that he wasn't deaf, he stammered — which of course he didn't do any more — and he was using the Meyer and Mair technique with the metronome beat in the form of a hearing aid. Now he was a willing patient who was also an experimenter, and there is no doubt that in his particular case — and, I know, in a number of other cases which have been reported in the literature — there have been quite satisfactory results. But I would say that we have to exercise extreme caution about making any assumptions that a particular stammerer, or someone with a particular speech defect, is our business at all. I say this because I think we must be careful that we do not interfere with any behaviour, the nature of which we do not properly understand.

Evidence so far suggests that all forms of psychotherapy are supportive, usually with a parent substitute situation. Behaviour therapy attempts laboratory objectivity, and in a sense perhaps attempts remoteness, in order not to get involved too much at the personal level. But clearly it is not able to maintain this role entirely. All forms of therapy demand varying degrees of activity on the part of the patient. What we do not know is what goes on between the sessions of whatever kind of therapy may be used. It is possible that the non-verbal forms of behaviour therapy would deprive the patient of the benefits of verbalization of the problem between sessions, and the more objective the behaviour therapy sessions may be, the less one would suppose the patient is able to carry the matter forward in the intervals.

If, on the other hand, behaviour therapy also withholds the

jargon of psychoanalysis from the patient, so the "inferiority complexes" and all the rest of the terms cease to be used by patients, then I think so much the better. At least, in other forms of psychotherapy, some continuous adjustive process may be assumed to take place between sessions. I think we are less certain that the patient is able to go on being active between sessions with the more remote or objective type of laboratory behaviour therapy.

Now I want to say a word about controlled experimental studies, to make comment about the difficulties of experimental studies at an objective level, despite Eysenck's claims in which he has the greatest confidence. I think we should look more carefully at the psychological situation which is set up for the patients in the control groups, unless they are totally unaware of their participation. We all know how frequently a patient for whom nothing has been done reports improvement after even a perfunctory interview. It seems that the process within the patient is activated by some intangible stimulus inherent in the interview situation. Time and again, on occasions when we have demonstrated testing procedures in the hospitals, patients have been said to exhibit improved behaviour in the wards during the following week, although nothing seriously has been done to reconstruct life for the individual or to do anything in the way of therapy. We cannot get away from this fact, that when we interview people, we do something to them.

We can certainly look to behaviour therapy for some information of a more objective character because of the kinds of methods used, but one notes very frequently in the reports on behaviour therapy that progress and improvement are accepted on the report of the patient. One gets strange reports from patients, of course. I remember observing an operant conditioning procedure with an elderly chronic schizophrenic patient in London. When he had his hand full of tokens from lever pulling, to which he applied himself assiduously, I said to him, "Do you find this treatment does you any good?" He said, "I'm not quite sure, but I think so." Well, you take what you like out of that. To me it is a warning that removal of symptoms (going through the motions in a negative sense) can please the experimenter. One writer has said that improvement in the patient reinforces the therapist.

Unless generalization takes place, it is unlikely that much has been achieved in any specific symptom dismissal. But the behaviour therapist is increasingly adopting the more insightful processes of the dynamic psychotherapist, and in all probability the rapprochement will come from that side.

I want to say a word or two now about the process by which we carry out diagnosis. This is a question which I think is due for consideration. Whether or not there is a union of methods between other therapists and behaviour therapists, there is a growing tendency today to think more in terms of symptomatology than of diagnostic categories. If we emphasize the symptoms and do not classify, we are in danger perhaps of losing sight of the person — a point which Professor Whitlock made yesterday. If, however, we retain the classifications we run the risk of assuming symptoms because they belong to the category. The question is whether a review of our procedure is necessary, and I think that those of us who are in the clinical field are constantly aware of the necessity of re-orienting ourselves within this scope.

Now, in keeping with the words spoken by Dr. Nurcombe and Dr. McConaghy, I want to mention that from a psychological point of view, many of us tend to adhere to a more holistic approach to personality, and feel that the segmental studies are relatively unfinished. Whichever theroretical model we prefer, it must be admitted that certain traits or reactions are peculiarly resistant to modification, because they are involved in the broader aspects of the social person. The social person is not complete in the laboratory; he is there more as an individual and we do not see the social milieu to which he belongs. He has interpersonal relations, he has his own self-concept, which he is very rarely able to convey to us. There is the mode of his upbringing, his religious sanctions, his conscience, his taboos, his beliefs, his superstitions, his feelings of inferiority, his educational backwardness and very often his poor and inadequate sex education. It is inconceivable that removal of any one symptom can, within a limited period — even of the maximum amount of time used in any behaviour therapy procedure — materially alter the patient's overall adjustment, his status in his social group, and so on, unless some other process goes on concurrently.

This brings up a very important consideration for all forms of therapy, which is the fact that no therapist can conscientiously and honestly believe that his concept of what is best for the patient is entirely objective, or is entirely unrelated to his own attitudes and adjustment. Thus we find, if we are not careful, that judgments may be made about homosexual and heterosexual cathexis, which probably rely more on the fortuitous exigencies of the law of the land at the time than upon any particular needs of the individual who is the patient, or indeed upon the needs of the society of which he is a part. But perhaps this is one behavioural segment that would be better excluded for a time from the materia of psychoanalysis and consigned to various laboratories for more exact examination of its true nature, as a basis for modification.

This question of the role of the therapist brings up the concept of the rights of the individual. It goes without saying that the psychologist who indulges in behaviour therapy lightheartedly may well have to face a charge of "brainwashing", and for this reason alone Professor Whitlock's reluctance to have punishment administered in the name of therapy should not go unheeded. A tremendous responsibility rests upon any worker who decides to manipulate the current adjustment of another individual. I suggest that the likelihood that Rogerian methods will ever achieve a rapprochement with behaviour therapy is not great. It might be said that Rogers' methods go further than any others to preserve the rights and freedom of the individual.

Many of us consider that behaviour therapy, promising as it is, can have a limited application. Indeed, other methods of therapy have found themselves in the same boat, to the extent that many therapists are known to be somewhat selective about cases they will accept.

Whichever method is employed — but I think the matter is more urgent in regard to behaviour therapy — the need for medical diagnosis cannot be overstressed. We shall never know how many unfortunate patients have been subjected to some form or other of psychotherapy for what to them connotes a mental disorder of their own making, because of no prior medical examination. They say they are ashamed to admit their behaviour or symptom to their doctor, when in fact, if only they would admit this behaviour, the doctor might have access to information which would lead him to a medical diagnosis. Eysenck himself has been outspoken about the need for careful selection of cases for behaviour therapy. I am reminded of various kinds of patients who might be subjected to the "pressures" of behavioural methods, with disastrous results which at least could not be described as therapeutic; for example, the hypertensive, the brain-damaged, or the stammerer whose simple symptom should happen to have more complex causation.

One thinks of the young woman in Illinois who was variously subjected to forms of therapy (and almost castigation) with various diagnoses of schizophrenia, depression and obsessive-compulsive neurosis. Medical analysis ultimately disclosed that she was reacting violently to massive intakes of beet sugar, to which she was strongly allergic. Complete withdrawal of beet destroyed the symptoms. The same experimenter, Theron G. Randolph, found that a number of alcoholics (who might have been subjected to behaviour therapy) were addicted to Scotch whisky (containing American beet sugar), but showed no addiction to other spirits. I can't help wondering if Professor Hammer's burping patient was ever tested for achlorhydria!

So far as enuresis is concerned, I have never been able to see this as a single symptom. Removing the habit system gives relief indeed. But other more complex habit systems are also already established and are more far reaching within the total adjustment. I refer to the status of the patient in his family and his peripheral social milieu. He is not an enuretic. He is a person who for some reason lacks capacity for control. He is adjusted to a self-concept involving uniqueness of behaviour, protectedness, feelings of guilt, etc. Withdrawal may be an established reaction. He may be regarded as somewhere between a protected infant and a pariah who lies concealed from public view. All this cannot be changed just by stopping bed wetting. This is not intended to mean that the mechanical methods commonly employed are undesirable, but rather that by themselves these methods are in danger of leaving an insecure, immature patient whose present relief masks his other therapeutic needs.

Finally I feel it only right to say that the application of learning and unlearning methods was current in psychotherapeutic practice many years before such terms as desensitization were borrowed from the pathology laboratory. I remember some years ago a case of very persistent and long-standing obsessive-compulsive symptomatology, who had been subjected to a wide variety of abortive treatments including the pre-war cardiazol shock, chemotherapy, and attempted hypnosis before she was referred to me, by the last of a number of doctors all of whom were tired of trying to help the case. Each successive treatment would seem to have stimulated further displacement of the original phobic reaction, until a formidable 133 items of compulsive nightly behaviours had accumulated. Each item had associated anxiety, but some sort of hierarchical importance could be developed.

(a) The list was made.

(b) The items were classified by the patient into groups according to severity of anxiety and proximity of objects.

(c) Voluntary inhibition, per week, was agreed on, starting with the least severe, mostly in groups.

(d) After one year, the top of the list was reached, viz. the close and personal items. These, too, were clearly displacements from more basic reactions, but became easier to control as they were approached. Without concurrent re-education and other constructive procedures, these "elimination stakes" would have achieved little, if anything, because these were activities of a supportive character, upon which she depended.

There was another phase of this case which also reacted well to what would now be called behaviour therapy: the question of a real phobia concerned with trams, trains and tunnels. The first thing the patient was asked to do was to take a ride in a tram or a train for one stop only. This went on to one stop and return, then to two stops, two stops and return, and so on. Eventually, we got the patient through a tunnel and after some practice in the tunnel we found that she was able to cope with public transport whenever necessary. It took another year or so to deal with this.

Now the other thing you may find of some interest, because it is perhaps a little outrageous, is that the dreams of this patient were also part of her symptomatology. They were of compulsive and nightmare proportions. Regarding these dreams as symptoms, I decided to try to dismiss the symptoms. The first thing I asked the patient to do was to write, verbatim as it were, her recollection of the dreams upon waking, however many dreams there might be, but not to attempt to turn them into a story or to elaborate them. Many of her reports were hardly more than phrases of remembered perceptions, and so on. No attempt at reconstruction or interpretation of the dreams was made, although it looked fairly clear that there was a very strong sexual basis to it all, which would have fitted into a psychoanalytic approach. However, if questioning was provoked by the patient, then some discussion went on. The themes, as I said, were repetitive. Suddenly there would come the time — which I had been waiting for — when the patient would recognize that a persistent theme had ceased to occur. This happened with quite a number of frightening sorts of dreams where it would appear that by mulling over them, writing them down and speaking them, and in this way passing them over in what might be called a transference situation, the patient had managed to get rid of the necessity to dream these particular themes. I might mention, in conclusion of this matter, that there was one dream in which the patient always was almost strangled, but never quite strangled, because she woke up before it happened. Different people were trying to strangle her in different dreams, but the theme recurred over and over. Then I woke up to what might be going on. I realized that when I questioned her further in another circumstance there were also physical symptoms being reported. She had a nasty taste in her mouth, she felt that she couldn't breathe, she had a frontal headache. When she was treated for sinusitis, the dream ceased to occur.

Well, these are facts and comments that one can make, and many of the dynamic psychiatrists of the pre-war days were in fact attempting these very procedures. I mention this in some detail now because I feel that perhaps this is a way in which immediate rapprochement and compromise are going on, and can go further, and I would hope that both fields, the dynamic and the behaviour forms of therapy, would benefit from each other.

CONCLUSIONS

I have tried in this brief statement to show that:

(a) The methods of behaviour therapy (in principle) can be allied with other methods of treatment.

(b) All possible care should be taken in selection of cases for any particular treatment.

(c) Mere removal of symptoms without a sound theoretical basis for broader supportive therapy is a questionable procedure except in the simplest context.

(d) Segmental approach to personality structure is not adequate for therapy in its present state.

(e) Prolonged follow-up procedure should be an obligation inherent in publication of reports.

(f) More care is required in use of terms, e.g. phobia.

(g) With Professor Yates, I agree that behavioural methods should be versatile and derived from broader contexts than that of learning theories alone.

and

(h) The present state of genetics, medicine, psychology, psychiatry, and other allied disciplines, e.g. speech therapy, occupational therapy, is such that none of us can do without a greater degree of interdisciplinary co-operation, and that the traffic should be two-way.

SEMINAR THREE : **PAPER THREE**

Dr. N. McConaghy

Though asked in this seminar to discuss differences between dynamically orientated and behaviour therapy, and in particular to stress the advantages of behaviour therapy, I have not felt able to do this exactly. For one thing, I consider behaviour therapy to be a form of therapy which is used in the context of a psychotherapeutic relationship, and in the handling of that relationship one is influenced by dynamic principles. For another, the type of patient for whom behaviour therapy seems suitable as the major form of treatment differs from one who is suitable for dynamically orientated psychotherapy as the major therapy. In brief, I do not see these forms of therapy as alternatives. Each has characteristic differences and I shall restrict myself to discussing these.

Firstly, behaviour therapy accepts the relevance of conventional scientific methodology, as used in the behavioural sciences, to all aspects of its theory and practice. Hypotheses will not be accepted until predictions from them are demonstrated to be valid in experiments where the relevant variables are appropriately controlled, if necessary employing a control group, statistical evaluation of the resultant data, and other such techniques.

Psychodynamic therapy is more likely to stress the limitations and inappropriateness of conventional scientific methodology. Reliance is put upon the training and experience of the therapist to determine the validity of his conclusions and to decide whether changes in the patient's behaviour are the result of the therapist's manipulations, rather than due to other variables.

In view of the stress placed by Freud on the basic irrationality of man's mental processes and the much greater role of unconscious than conscious mechanisms in determining these, it has always struck me as something of a paradox that he and his school have felt so confident of the validity of the conclusions reached by the speculations of the conscious mind, albeit one trained in an awareness of the unconscious factors influencing it.

The attitude of the behaviour therapist is the conventional scientific one that one cannot by speculation alone determine if one has reached a valid conclusion. The human mind is capable of such ingenuity that there is no set of observations for which it cannot find several logically compelling and intellectually overpowering explanations — all of them mutually incompatible. It was of course precisely for this reason that scientific method was introduced, since by philosophical speculation man could not arrive at a theory as to the nature of reality which enabled him to predict and manipulate its changes.

Perhaps we can summarize this characteristic by the statement that dynamic therapy, having stressed the vulnerability of human mentation, is nevertheless prepared to use it as the major tool in understanding and controlling human behaviour; behaviour therapy, while suspicious of the dynamic theories as to the nature of human mentation, is not prepared to rely on mentation alone without employing safeguards evolved over the last several centuries. The good behaviour therapist therefore would be appalled at anyone with pretensions to belonging to their ranks speculating about the nature of behaviour therapy in contrast to psychodynamic therapy, without any means of adequately testing the validity of these speculations.

The second characteristic of behaviour therapy is related to the first. It is that behaviour therapy and its related theory does not aim at providing a comprehensive theory of normal and abnormal behaviour. As with other conventional sciences, this is seen only as a hoped-for long-term goal. The immediate goal is the exploration of that frontier of unknown knowledge that borders the known and which therefore is capable of being investigated. Psychodynamic therapy and theory do aim at providing a complete and unified explanation of behaviour. By virtue of its methodology — speculating about all aspects of observed behaviour and how they can be fitted into the general framework of psychodynamic theory, with plausibility the test of fit — this is of course possible.

From this, the third characteristic follows. Behaviour therapy is prepared to analyse and treat detailed aspects of behaviour in isolation from the personality of the patient as a whole. Techniques may be evolved to attack a particular symptom without attention necessarily being paid to scientifically unconfirmed theories as to the possible etiology or significance of the symptom in relation to the patient's whole personality. Considerable time may be spent on a treatment programme with a quite trivial therapeutic goal if this is considered of theoretical importance. Stopping a schizophrenic patient from hoarding towels or training another to use simple vocalizations may be carried out to test some prediction without expecting the patient's behaviour as a whole to show significant modification. It is expected of course that the patient's needs and dignity as a human being and his personal happiness are not jeopardized.

This preparedness to treat the symptom in isolation does not mean that behaviour therapists do not believe there may be no underlying disturbance of higher nervous activity, or neurosis. The concept of the symptom's being the neurosis may be adequate for some learning theories, and is particularly relevant to a behaviourist approach. However, far from the majority of behaviour therapists seem to be behaviourists and I, for one, regard it as most unfortunate that the name "behaviour therapy" has become accepted for the application of learning theory principles to treatment. Certainly from Pavlovian theory, one would expect general neurotic disturbances of the nervous system to underlie many isolated symptoms.

In contrast to the focussing on the isolated symptom characterizing behaviour therapy, psychodynamic therapists, in line with their view of regarding and attempting to explain behaviour as a whole, tend to treat the patient as a whole and regard it as time-wasting, if not dangerous, to treat the isolated symptom. With this aim, the concomitant rejection of conventional scientific method becomes essential. Scientific method can only operate by a piecemeal approach to an entire area of knowledge — by limitation of the goal to one particular problem. One must reject scientific method in the investigation of human behaviour if one believes that human beings function so much as a whole that the attempt to isolate one aspect of human behaviour and control the variables affecting this aspect will introduce such distortion as to invalidate the results.

These opposing attitudes produce the next characteristic difference. Psychodynamic therapy utilizes the technique of the analysis of interpersonal relationships for all patients. Modifications of this basic technique will vary with the relationship, rather than with particular symptoms. Behaviour therapy utilizes different techniques, the choice of which is largely determined by the nature of the symptom being treated.

Finally, behaviour therapy tends to give a high priority to the

99

evaluation of its results and the problems involved in estimating this. The dynamic psychotherapist is more likely to be content with his own subjective assessment of the results of his methods.

In summary, I consider the characteristic differences in behaviour therapy and psychodynamic therapy result from the acceptance of conventional scientific methodology by the former and its rejection by the latter. This situation is completely understandable historically. Psychodynamic therapy came into being to deal with the situation that patients had to be treated for behavioural disturbances in the absence of any scientific knowledge as to how to treat their individual symptoms. In the course of relating to and attempting to help such people a vast amount of observational data has accumulated which cannot yet be scientifically investigated. Finding such data of value in the handling of his patients in day-to-day practice, the dynamic psychotherapist is not going to reject it because it is not demonstrably valid scientifically. To him this only demonstrates the limitation and irrelevance of the scientific method.

Behaviour therapy has appeared at a time when sufficient scientific knowledge is available to devise methods of treating individual psychiatric symptoms and to evaluate the results in terms of relief of symptoms. Such therapy must seem crude and insightless to the psychotherapist, who has learnt to view the patient as a whole complex person and who, in the light of this view, can manipulate his relationship with the patient in a technically highly skilful and sophisticated, if largely intuitive, fashion.

As I stated initially, I do not view these two forms of therapy as alternatives. For the foreseeable future, there will be patients suited to dynamic psychotherapy — in my view especially those with personality disorders or in situational difficulties, and there will be patients suited to behaviour therapy — in my view, the anxious, the obsessive-compulsive, those with disturbances of sexual behaviour and with psychogenic disorders of voluntary movement.

As I believe the word to be the most powerful influence on human behaviour, I find it impossible to imagine, even ultimately, a society without some form of verbal psychotherapy, though as to whether it will be dynamic psychotherapy I take leave to have reservations.

DISCUSSION

Professor Yates: Before throwing open the discussion, I would like to have the privilege of making just one comment. I want to make this comment because it is one which has been made several times in the literature, and I think it does raise a very important point. Dr. Nurcombe argued — I think he argued it himself, but if not he was repeating the argument of others — that behaviour therapists adopt the procedures they do adopt because they are incapable of establishing satisfactory personal relationships with their patients. This has been thought to be the essence of psychiatry. Either they are unable to do this, or they are unwilling to do it. On the other hand, Dr. Harwood told us that Dr. Lovibond obtained his results from behaviour therapy precisely because he was able to establish a successful personal relationship. And in general, critics of behaviour therapy have argued that such results as have been obtained are not due to the particular methods they have used, but rather to the establishment of successful interpersonal relationships with their patients.

Now I do not see that these two propositions are reconcilable. If it is true that behaviour therapists are incompetent in establishing interpersonal relationships with their patients, then I don't see that it is legitimate to attribute the successes that are obtained to such an establishment. In fact, in the case of Dr, Lovibond's boy, which Dr. Harwood specifically mentioned. one would have to make the further assumption that in spite ol Lovibond's general incompetence in establishing interpersonaf relationships, he was actually better at establishing an inter- personal relationship with this child than the psychiatrists who had previously treated the child. They had apparently rejected the child and refused to readmit him to the hospital. These kinds of *ad hoc* explanations of the results of behaviour therapy seem to me to be quite illegitimate, and since this point has been made on several occasions, I think that it is a matter for comment and consideration. In saying this, incidentally, I do not wish for one minute to deny the importance or significance of the relationship between the psychologist or psychiatrist and his patient, nor its possible effect upon the treatment, but this is something for experimental investigation, not for *ad hoc* judgments which happen to show up behaviour therapists or psychiatrists in a particularly favourable or unfavourable light.

Dr. Nurcombe: I'd like to answer Professor Yates's comment. I think Professor Yates rather missed the context in which I was speaking. I was trying to point out that there seems to be a mutual building up and attacking of straw-men in the two camps. On the one hand we have the stereotype of the woolly-minded sentimentalist, the psychodynamicist, and on the other hand the tough-minded behaviour therapist who avoids basic encounters. I don't personally believe this is so, although it may be the case with individuals. I was pointing this out as an example of the ridiculous, artificial sort of combat system which has been built up as a result of the polemics.

I support Professor Yates's plea for the need for experimental validation of the different types of therapy. The difficulty is in measuring this sort of thing, both quantitatively and qualitatively, but one cannot ignore it.

Professor Yates: The classic instance recently has been the demonstration by Rogers' own students, in particular Charles Truax, using Rogers' own case data, and with Rogers' approval (which is to his credit), that the one thing non-directive therapy is not, is non-directive. It is quite clear that non-directive therapy is directive, and that the therapist — in this case Rogers — changes the verbal behaviour of the patient by giving or withholding reinforcing verbal behaviour on his part. This indicates quite clearly that in this kind of work the actual verbal behaviour of the patient is changed by what the therapist does, i.e. the therapist and the patient interact, and quite clearly, as I think Dr. Harwood indicated before, the patient is experimenting with the experimenter; he is modifying the behaviour of the experimenter. It is a two-way process, and what we really want to know is what exactly is going on in the psychotherapeutic relationship, between, for instance, the psychiatrist and his patient. In what way is the psychiatrist influencing his patient's behaviour, even though he may not be aware of it, and in what way is the patient influencing the psychiatrist? If the psychiatrist is quite happy with the present situation in which he produces changes in his patient without knowing how it's done, and therefore without knowing how he can economize his treatment, and carry it out on a more rational basis, then that's fine, and the whole subject will stand still. But if we really want to know what goes on in a psychotherapeutic situation, then I must again assert that there is only one possible way of doing it, and that is by manipulating the variables that enter into this situation, unless we think the whole thing is so irrational that we cannot do this.

Mr. I. Hills: Have any experimental approaches been made with the aim of pinpointing stages in the treatment of a patient undergoing psychotherapy where he is particularly receptive to behaviour therapy?

Dr. Nurcombe: I think this is an important point. I think there does come a time in, say, insight therapy, when the patient understands the situation fairly well, and a choice has to be made, or a number of choices. For example the choice that is most appropriate may involve action in which the person is quite inexperienced. In discussion yesterday, one of the members of the audience was telling me about a boy, a schizophrenic, who had improved, but had never used money, had never been to a shop, had never been on a train, and so on. This, of course, required re-educative techniques. I also draw your attention again to the work of Crisp using Kelly's grid technique for assessing the way in which the patient structures the woild around him conceptually, and of measuring changes in this structuring, during the course of therapy. I think that it is only by these sorts of techniques that we can meet this problem At the moment it would have to be intuitive.

SEMINAR FOUR: FUTURE OF BEHAVIOUR THERAPY

SEMINAR FOUR: **PAPER ONE**

Alcoholism

Dr. R. B. Milton

A recurring problem in this area is one of definition. What is alcoholism? Can we accept it as a legitimate condition? Is it simply a convenient label? Do we look on excessive drinking as a disease, as many alcoholics do, or do we look on this as a symptom? We can say either that alcoholics are unhappy because they drink, a view that is supported by most alcoholics and their families, or that alcoholics drink excessively because they are disturbed, because basically they are unhappy.

Both of these viewpoints exist in much more sophisticated form and both enjoy wide acceptance. Most people who are involved in this field, however, usually adopt a position half way between the two. If we accept one or other of these views, we incline to a particular approach in treatment. If we accept that alcoholics are disturbed because they drink, then it would seem that behaviour therapy is a legitimate kind of treatment to use. If we think that alcoholics are disturbed people and drink because they are disturbed, then surely we attempt to deal with their disturbance. This is a very naïve, oversimplified sort of statement, but I present it because many people working with alcoholics state the problem in these terms.

There is no doubt that we must regard this whole complex, or syndrome, or illness — alcoholism — as the result of a very complicated set of social and interpersonal circumstances in each case. It seems fairly obvious also that an individual comes to rely on the anxiety-relieving properties of alcohol, and that this constitutes a learnt pattern of behaviour, regardless of the factors that cause the initial anxiety.

107

I do not think it matters in itself that one learns to allay one's basic and everyday anxieties through the use of alcohol. In doing this, however, one seems to lose one's other methods of dealing with everyday anxiety. As we fall back on one method for dealing with all problems, so do we unlearn or forget these other methods of dealing with those problems — they fall into disuse. This reduced ability to handle everyday anxiety without the use of alcohol increases the individual's basic anxiety. Significant people — family or employer for example — are going to get disturbed and are going to make the individual feel disturbed about his excessive drinking. We can be fairly safe in saying that some kind of a vicious circle develops, where alcohol is used with increasing frequency in a wider and wider variety of circumstances. The more it is used this way, however, the more restricted become the individual's other outlets. And in addition, the excessive use of alcohol tends to bring problems of its own, through physical upset and family disturbance and social rejection. The alcoholic deals with the subsequent anxiety by taking more alcohol. Thus we get some kind of a pattern of behaviour set up.

In this context, it seems that we could use something of behaviour therapy, since to some degree we have to deal directly with the pattern of drinking and the disturbance which arises immediately from this. And this is what you find if you ever go to an Alcoholics Anonymous meeting. The first thing the alcoholics focus on is that they are alcoholic, and the next thing they focus on is their drinking pattern. To them, alcoholism is either a learnt pattern of behaviour, or a pattern of behaviour which results from some physical disorder. To them it is not a pattern of behaviour that results from underlying emotional disturbance.

What kind of behaviour therapy are we going to use? There was one example of massed practice used in the United States a good many years ago, called the Keeley cure — perhaps someone has heard of this — which consisted of putting alcoholics in some sort of institution — it was a very pleasant institution because these people had a lot of money — and letting them drink as they liked, so that they got so sick that they decided they would never drink again. Well, it killed some patients, and some got better, but this is what happens to alcoholics anyway.

Now there are all sorts of very interesting and ingenious techniques being developed in attempts to make alcohol unacceptable to patients. Many people will be aware of these, and I may be going over familiar ground by mentioning them. One of the earliest and best known is the production of vomiting upon giving a dose of alcohol. This sounds a fairly simple sort of treatment, but in practice it proves fairly complex. The patient is usually brought into a room, is given some sort of pleasant association with alcohol, is given a small dose of alcohol, and at the same time is given an injection of emetine or apomorphine, some drug that has a particularly alarming and disturbing effect — the disturbing effect is that the patient vomits, copiously and for a long time. Admittedly it is very unpleasant and very messy.

Another method which is much more refined and simple is the use of electric shock coupled with the administration of alcohol. A more recently developed method, which has been reported in the last twelve months, involves a drug called scoline — this is a drug that immediately relaxes the whole of the body musculature so that the patient is immediately unable to breathe, feels a sense of impending death, and as you can imagine, is very disturbed and upset by this, because he is fully conscious throughout the whole procedure. The patient is given a smell of alcohol at the same time as a dose of scoline is administered. Usually it is not repeated, since the patients do not seem to want it to happen too often. Another method involves the use of Antabuse, a drug developed some years ago which reacts with alcohol to produce a toxic substance which causes vomiting and shortage of breath. In this case, patients are usually loaded with the dose of Antabuse, given a test dose of alcohol, allowed to experience what it is like, and then continued on Antabuse for some time.

Now all these methods have some effectiveness, but the main purpose, it seems to me, is to develop an aversion to alcohol itself. A more sophisticated version of these methods is to try to develop aversion towards the pleasant phantasies associated with alcohol. And one method that I shall describe is to produce in the patient a pleasant state of reminiscence about his previous drinking episodes, and the wonderful way he feels when he first starts to take a couple of drinks, and at this stage he is given an electric shock. This does seem to me to be an advance on simply conditioning the patient against alcohol itself.

These methods do have some success although at this stage it is impossible to assess this precisely, because of the great difficulty in following cases for any length of time. This is one consideration which is not fully recognized by people who have used these methods, that evaluation of the methods entails very adequate history taking. For example, there was someone I heard of in the United States a few months ago who was using a conditioning technique but spent some thirty hours with each patient before beginning the conditioning technique. The implications here are

109

that perhaps there was a great deal coming out of the relationship with the therapist. We cannot be more definite than this. A great deal of contact, however, may be necessary to supplement the conditioning technique.

One of the dangers that has been ascribed to these techniques is that, by interfering suddenly with an established pattern of behaviour, in this case drinking, we might precipitate heavier drinking to try and overcome the conditioning, or the use of drugs as substitutes, or even suicidal attempts. These things might happen, I do not have any evidence on them. But it does seem likely that without adequate preparation or without adequate co-operation of patients, we may cause more disturbance than is appropriate at the time, which may result in dangerous consequences for the patient.

My personal criticism of these methods is that they tend to be too far removed from the patient's everyday life. They have too much of an aura of mysticism and technicality about them. Although we cannot say that alcoholics constitute particular personality types, one thing that we often see is a kind of dependency. Alcoholics invariably say: "Please cure me with some drug or some food, or something else." This kind of treatment would fit in neatly with the approach that many alcoholics have to their own progress. They are looking for an easy way out of something which perhaps others of us have had to sort out in a much more difficult way. They are looking for an easy way to overcome basic anxiety.

I think a further practical point about these methods is that their appropriate administration usually requires a fair amount of time, per patient, from professional staff. Other methods have been developed for treating alcoholics which demand far less time. There are also dangers if the methods of apomorphine or emetine are used. People can often react very badly to these drugs. These dangers of course do not exist with the electric shock method.

We can ascribe a large amount of alcoholism to conditioned behaviour. But this learning has taken place over a long period and in an amazingly complex variety of circumstances. Most people call these circumstances life. The conditions of upbringing and later existence are probably what make us what we are now. Those of us who are alcoholics have become this way probably because we have been conditioned to it, over a very long time, and in all sorts of ways. These ways of conditioning have not taken place in the laboratory, but most of the conditioning methods of treatment are relevant only to a very narrow area of the patient's life. It seems that if we are going to condition alcoholics for therapeutic purposes, the place to do it is in situations as complex as those in which the original learning occurred. If we can bring to bear on patients appropriate forces or conditioning methods in contexts similar to those in which excessive drinking first occurred, then surely this may be better than to try to condition patients to one specific and isolated area of behaviour, which is, say, their drinking itself.

We can say that alcoholics become the way they are through their many experiences in life. The way to unlearn or disregard these patterns of excessive drinking behaviour is in a context which we can describe as a normal life situation. I know I can be criticized for trying to describe normal life, but when you are working with patients you have to try to make some standards yourself. There is simply no other way of approaching patients. It seems that we must have some kind of conditioning related as closely as possible to normal existence. I feel that many of these methods are involved in ordinary community therapy, and that we may think of these as methods of producing insight, methods of retraining patients.

I would like to cite a few examples of some of the aspects of treatment at the Wacol Rehabilitation Clinic and at the Alcoholism Clinic at the Royal Brisbane Hospital, which I would perhaps see as conditioning techniques.

The basic thing that we aim for amongst our patients is acceptance of responsibility. We can look on alcoholism to an extent as an avoidance of responsibility, avoidance of everyday anxiety through drinking, until eventually this anxiety cannot be dealt with at all. We attempt as far as possible to have our patients in a situation where they get immediate benefit from accepting responsibility. Now we do not do this on the basis of the individual patient. Alcoholics are extremely good manipulators themselves. If we reward patients for taking responsibility individually, they can fool us nearly every time by conforming with what they think we want from them. What we attempt is to get not just one patient to conform but a body of patients. This means that if we have fifty patients in residence at Wacol, these patients are put in a position where they get benefit from accepting responsibility as a whole, where they get some sort of detriment from refusing responsibility.

About twelve months ago we had a dispute between the patients in their kitchen duties — patients normally serve their own food at this unit, and they organize their own rosters for this. There was a dispute and they said, "Look, we want the staff to organize this for us." We said, "No, we do not think we should do this.

111

We think you are quite capable of doing this organizing yourselves, and we will not accept this responsibility. But what we
will do is take over the kitchen duties from you ourselves, if you
cannot run them yourselves." We also said that since the staff
was limited, meals would not be served on time as they would be
if the patients were serving themselves, that this was a responsibility they could take, and if they did not take it, then probably
things would not go as well as if they did accept this.

Now this can be looked on as primarily a manipulative technique
on the part of the staff, but on the other hand you see that there
will be a very mixed reaction from the patients. Some will say,
"Let the staff do it", others will say, "No, let us do it ourselves,
as we want our meals on time." What we are seeing happen is
that the patients who are not willing to accept this responsibility
are receiving social pressures which are very potent from those
who do want to accept it, and they are accepting it from people
with whom they would more normally attempt to escape the
responsibility. These are their peers with whom they would at
other times drink. It is these people who are saying to them, "Now
this is a responsible kind of activity and I think we should accept
it." Under these circumstances they are saying, "We will reject
you socially if you do not do this." And this is not something
that happens just once, it happens over and over again. I think we
can regard this as a kind of conditioning.

Another example relates to patients who persistently phantasize
about their drinking and the pleasures that it used to give them.
To an extent we can view this as a continuation of the pleasant
phantasies associated with drinking, and patients have, in the
months the clinic has been in existence, brought in their own
controls over this sort of thing. Initially, at the unit which preceded
this one, patients would spend a great deal of their time talking
about their everyday drinking experiences, and how good these
were. Social changes have taken place amongst the patients now
so that if anyone refers to drinking in this way they receive
immediate social rejection. Here is a kind of social conditioning
which is taking place all the time. It is not related to alcohol but
to the phantasies associated with it. The patient begins to re-
minisce about the wonderful time he had getting drunk and sick
and getting drunk again, and someone immediately rejects him,
and it will be someone he knows and thinks something of. It
is not something that happens in an immediate conditioning
situation, it is the kind of conditioning that goes on all the while.

There is one point I would like to make in conclusion. Although
we can view some of these techniques as conditioning methods,

it is very hard for us to try and assess how effective they are — whether they really are conditioning, or whether they are techniques for the patients to gain more insight. It would seem that one of the requests that treatment units of this nature could make to people who are doing research is to design research models, so that it is not necessary or obligatory to make an experiment of this kind of work, but so that we can apply methods to investigate the work as it is being done. At the present moment, it seems that what is happening in this kind of situation is so complex and to do any kind of research on it is so difficult that we immediately say, "Well, it is very hard to design an experiment, let us do something much more simple like giving patients apomorphine treatment." I think the request that we who are working in the treatment field would make is for someone, sometime, to design a research model so that we can better assess the kind of work we are doing.

SEMINAR FOUR: **PAPER TWO**
General Clinical Practice

Mr. J. C. Winship

Not surprisingly perhaps, much of what I propose to say has already been said, either yesterday or this morning. If it is any consolation I have blue-pencilled parts of my original notes and I intend to stick closely to what is left so as to take up a minimum of time, leaving more time for discussion which I think, in the circumstances, would be much more valuable, especially in the light of what Professor Yates had to say yesterday. Indeed, if he is right, and I very much fear that he may be, then of course I need take up very little of your time — there is for the time being no place for so-called behaviour therapy in routine clinical practice. However, I shall do as other speakers did yesterday and for the purpose of this exercise talk about what I think most people have in mind when they refer to behaviour therapy.

There is of course no simple and clear-cut answer as to what is likely to be the future for behaviour therapies in general clinical practice. Yesterday and again this morning we have heard discussed the whys and wherefores, the pros and cons of behaviour therapy and its relationship with psychotherapy. The difficulty is that the status of behaviour therapy is still very uncertain; its effectiveness has not been proven to everyone's satisfaction, though by the same token neither has it been discredited.

Beech[1] says, "There is a dearth of critical evidence concerning the efficacy of behaviour therapy." Meyer and Gelder[2] state, "Considerable claims have been made for behaviour therapy but the evidence for its effectiveness is conflicting." However, each goes on to say in effect that even if behaviour therapy is still in its infancy, even if the techniques employed and the theories from

114

which they derive are raw, undeveloped and unsophisticated, behaviour therapy has come to stay as a useful adjunct in the clinic. Meyer and Crisp[3] add the warning that it may fall into disrepute if it is uncritically accepted as a ready-made and well-established form of treatment, that if theoretical and practical advances are to be made, then a more rigorous and planned experimental approach is needed to many of its problems.

With these reservations in mind it is pertinent to ask with what groups of patients behaviour therapy is being used. Here again one is in difficulties in so far as an assessment of its usefulness in practice is concerned. Is behaviour therapy the treatment of choice, as Wolpe[4] claims, for all or most neuroses, or is it of use only in quite limited areas of disturbance? If the latter, then clearly its usefulness in practice is relatively quite circumscribed.

Wolpe puts up a quite spirited defence for the effectiveness of behaviour therapy in the treatment of the more complex neuroses. He begins his report with the categorical statement, "In recent years it has become widely known that behaviour therapy is effective in the treatment of neurosis", and then continues:

> However, in my mind, this knowledge has come to be hedged around by erroneous qualifications of which the commonest are (a) that behaviour therapy leaves the "deep" causes of neurosis untouched, and (b) that it is successful with "mono-symptomatic" and allegedly simple cases like phobias but not with the more complex neuroses such as obsessions and character neuroses.

Time does not permit more than a passing glance at his arguments, but there is much in them that is quite bothersome. For instance, talking about the character neuroses he says, "In the great majority of such cases the deviant behaviour is secondary to anxiety whose sources need to be ferreted out. If this is not done then therapeutic failure can almost be guaranteed." The question in my mind is how does one succeed in ferreting out significant information from a patient, and especially one of this ilk, unless and until one has established a working relationship with him.

Referring to a particular patient Wolpe says she was treated by "sustained encouragement of self-expression", that she was strongly urged to express her legitimate demands and that "she soon grasped the reasonableness of this and made efforts to comply". While it is true that she was being treated at one and the same time by desensitization it is difficult to escape the conclusion that Wolpe was using methods and techniques similar to or identical with those used by psychotherapists. Indeed, one of his severest critics, Alistair Forrest, has said of him that he gives the impression of being intensely interested in his patients and that he is probably a very good therapist. I suppose by that Dr. Forrest meant "psychotherapist". Perhaps Dr. Wolpe would see this as a back-handed compliment, but to the extent that it is true, it clouds the issue as to how much the personal equation is a potent factor in the therapy. There is some research evidence to suggest that it is. Meyer and Gelder stated that the single factor most relevant to the outcome of behaviour therapy was the patient-therapist relationship and that, equally, feelings which the therapist formed in relation to the patient influenced the course of treatment just as the counter-transference does in psychotherapy.

All of this might reasonably be considered, in practice, as a distinction without a difference — therapy is therapy, what works is good, but it is one of many crucial differentiations if one is attempting to see what kind of therapy is responsible for what. Perhaps I have over-laboured the point, but if, in fact, Wolpe's concern is well founded — if, that is, behaviour therapy is effective only with "monosymptomatic" and with allegedly simple cases such as phobias — then this, as I said earlier, gives behaviour therapy a quite restricted role in routine clinic work. That this could well be the situation seems a reasonable conclusion from the literature, much of it written subsequent to Wolpe's article.

One does find that the majority of reports on behaviour therapy are concerned with patients with relatively clear-cut abnormalities, that is, disorders in which the concepts of stimulus and response are relatively quite well defined. Not surprisingly therefore, the number of phobic patients treated by behaviour therapy is greater than that for other types of patients. A quite typical statement is that by Hain, Butcher and Stevenson[5] who say, "We selected patients for this treatment who in general experienced anxiety in specific situations, in short, patients who had phobias..." In point of fact there are as yet even with phobic patients few acceptable criteria for the selection of patients in the sense of giving any reliable prediction as to the probable outcome of behaviour therapy with a particular patient. The position as found by Meyer and Crisp is that some apparently straightforward cases failed to respond well to treatment — contrariwise, a few quite complex phobias both in terms of current symptomatology, and in terms of complex historical development, responded well.

In general, however, there seems reason enough to believe that the group of patients which benefits most from behaviour therapy consists of those in whom anxiety develops in relatively specific conditions, i.e. in patients without widespread neurotic disturbance.

This is the conclusion of Cooper, Gelder and Marks[6] who reported on the results of behaviour therapy in the treatment of seventy-seven psychiatric patients. In summary they found that:

a) Their twenty-nine severe agoraphobics did slightly but not significantly better than their twenty-nine controls.

b) Twelve other phobics, as e.g. with phobias of animals, insects, or thunder, showed far more improvement than did eleven controls; this difference, which was significant at the end of treatment, diminished, however, and was no longer significant after one year's follow-up.

c) Results were poor in thirteen patients with writer's cramp and ten with obsessive rituals but their corresponding controls also did poorly.

d) Results were also poor in thirteen patients with miscellaneous conditions.

To the extent that the literature I've reported is reliable, one is entitled to ask, what then is the present status of behaviour therapy and its likely use in general clinical practice? This seems to be best summed up by two authors mentioned previously, Marks and Gelder,[7] and I propose to give you their conclusions verbatim. They state:

> The two approaches can be complementary, not conflicting — some patients require the first approach, others the second, and yet others require a combined treatment. There are some pointers to the clinical indications for separate or combined treatment. We use both approaches in appropriate cases.
>
> Patients can be referred for behaviour therapy when they have simple phobias, or enuresis or reading disabilities where careful inquiry fails to show accompanying emotional disturbance, with some cases of fetishism or of transvestism, or for other clearly delineated problems suitable for a behavioural regime.
>
> Patients can be referred for psychodynamic psychotherapy when their difficulties appear to relate to unexpressed feelings and problems in interpersonal adjustment. A few patients can have both types of treatment when the problems require a combined approach. Psychotherapists can ask for their patients to have some behaviour therapy and vice versa.

They conclude that "both approaches are here to stay and it is to be hoped that each will develop".

Finally, I might mention the report by Hain, Butcher and Stevenson which presents a much rosier picture than those given by Cooper, Gelder and Marks and Meyer and Crisp. The overall improvement rate for the group was 78 per cent. What is more, on follow-up (average time of one year), of those who had shown improvement initially, 20 per cent were more improved (lessened severity of symptoms), 47 per cent had maintained their end of therapy status, 20 per cent were slightly worse, and 13 per cent had relapsed nearly completely. This however was a study without control groups.

Another criticism is that the two therapists involved did not hesitate to use "other techniques of therapy from time to time". "In the initial interview for evaluation, and in subsequent interviews also, the patient gave the therapist considerable information about his personal relationships and the stressful events of his life." Thus he undoubtedly derived benefits from the ventilation and clarification of certain issues of his life related to his symptoms.

So despite the fact that this last report on the surface seems so much more hopeful, I have doubts as to what credence can be given it. I think we are back in the position where, as I said earlier, or I think Meyer and Gelder said earlier, it is a question of combining both approaches, excluding neither one nor the other, but using whatever seems appropriate at the particular time, and for the particular case.

REFERENCES

1. Beech, H.R. (1963). Some theoretical and technical difficulties in the application of behaviour therapy. *Bull. Br. psychol. Soc.* **16,** 25-33.
2. Meyer, V. & Gelder, M.G. (1963). Behaviour therapy and phobic disorders. *Br. J. Psychiat.* **109,** 19-28.
3. Meyer, V. & Crisp, A.H. (1966). Some problems in behaviour therapy. *Br. J. Psychiat.* **112,** 367-81.
4. Wolpe, J. (1964). Behaviour therapy in complex neurotic states. *Br. J. Psychiat.* **110,** 28-34.
5. Hain, J., Butcher, R.H.G. & Stevenson, I. (1966). Systematic desensitization therapy: an analysis of results in twenty-seven patients. *Br. J. Psychiat.* **112,** 295-307.
6. Cooper, J.E., Gelder, M.G. & Marks, I.M. (1965). Results of behaviour therapy in seventy-seven psychiatric patients. *Br. med. J.* **1,** 1222-25.
7. Marks, I.M. & Gelder, M.G. (1965). A controlled retrospective study of behaviour therapy in phobic patients. *Br. J. Psychiat.* **111,** 561-73.

SEMINAR FOUR : **PAPER THREE**

Speech Correction

Professor A. J. Yates

As usual, when behaviour therapists talk about "speech correction" they are actually talking about stuttering, which is very unfortunate, because as speech therapists know stuttering is by no means the most common form of speech disorder. Unfortunately, behaviour therapists so far have largely confined themselves to stuttering, and so it is about stuttering that I am going to talk.

In recent work by behaviour therapists, there have been two quite different approaches tried, within quite different theoretical frameworks. I am not going to say very much about the first of these although some of you may not be very familiar with it; the second approach, to my mind, represents some of the most brilliant and outstanding work that has ever been done in the field of behaviour therapy. It has only recently been carried out and reported, and therefore I will concentrate on that, not only because it is more recent, but also because it has certain very important implications which have been rather strongly stressed in this symposium, and which, I think, represent one of the most important conclusions which will come out of the weekend.

Stuttering can be conceptualized in many different ways, of course, but two ways that I want to refer to today are in terms of speech as a servo-mechanistic process, that is, as controlled essentially by feedback processes resulting from speech itself, and secondly as a form of learnt behaviour which is maintained by its consequences on the environment, that is, maintained by events which it produces in the environment. We should notice that in neither case am I referring to the content of speech but rather the form of speech.

119

Before I go on to stuttering itself, I want to say that there is a great deal of experimental evidence now from the analysis and experimental control of normal speech which suggests that it is valuable to consider speech as a servo-mechanistic process. That is, the output, which is speech, like any other kind of response, such as walking or reading, feeds back information via various channels to the person, which tells him about the progress of his speech. After all, if we want to walk from Point A to Point B, we obviously must know, somehow or other, the successive positions of our limbs in space. If we did not know when our right leg was in front of our left leg, we would find it extremely difficult to locomote from A to B. Similarly in speech we must know how speech is progressing, so that we can emit one word-unit or speech-unit after another.

Speech is controlled[1] partly by events in the environment; for example, if the noise level in this room suddenly goes up, then the level of my speech will go up. But it is also controlled by internal feedback events, which are mediated through three channels essentially. We hear the sound of our own voice through the airborne channel, we hear it through the bone-conduction channel, and we also receive information from the stimulation arising from the actual movements of the musculature involved in speech. The one point I want to make about normal speech is that we now know that normal speech can be very severely disrupted if we interfere deliberately with feedback processes in one or other of the feedback channels. This is the condition which is known as delayed auditory feedback, in which instead of hearing the sound of his own voice with the usual delay of about one millisecond, the subject hears his own voice with an optimal delay of the order of 200 milliseconds. Under these conditions, very severe speech breakdown may be produced.

The one major experimental finding which I want to refer to here is that under these conditions, the subject has the problem essentially of attempting to restore the disrupted output-feedback relationship. One way in which a subject who is not too severely affected by delayed auditory feedback can achieve this is by the technique which is known as the "prolongation" of his speech, i.e he draws his speech out. What he does here essentially is to repeat speech units until such time as the delayed auditory feedback catches up with the output, and in this way he artificially restores the time relationships to a very considerable degree, though not entirely of course. The penalty for this is slowed up speech, but this situation seems to be more reinforcing than the alternative, which is the kind of disturbance that we normally see.

With respect to stuttering, the first approach is to regard stuttering as a form of disturbed feedback relationships;[2] it has been shown beyond any question that, with very few exceptions, all stutterers are capable of perfectly normal speech under appropriate conditions. The appropriate conditions are essentially that they shall not be able to perceive the low-frequency components of the sound of their own voice. If you stop a stutterer from listening to the sound of his own voice, he will stop stuttering and speak normally. When I say that, I mean just that; I do not mean that his speech improves somewhat, I mean that his speech becomes indistinguishable from normal speech. Cherry and Sayers[3] showed a long time ago that the effect is related to the perception of the low-frequency components of the sound of one's own voice which are mainly bone-conducted. It has been concluded, therefore, that stuttering is a perceptual defect associated with the perception of the low-frequency components of one's own voice.

There are a number of conditions, apart from preventing the subject from hearing the sound of his own voice by means of white noise, by which a stutterer can be enabled to speak normally. In a sense, his major problem is that he cannot learn, as it were, to speak normally, because he cannot stop stuttering. If you can artificially stop him from stuttering, it is argued, then if you give him sufficient practice in this normal speech, for which he has the capacity, but which is being interfered with continually by the faulty feedback channel, he would in fact be able to build up the feedback controlling pattern in the other channels to such a degree that they would overcome the faulty feedback channel. Cherry and Sayers developed the method of shadowing (which is now well known) in which the stutterer follows the speech of another person without actually seeing what he is reading, or the even simpler technique of simultaneous reading which will also abolish stuttering. They hoped that given sufficient practices of this kind, the stutterer would be able to build up adequate feedback controlling mechanisms of the kind that are developed in the young child, but which he apparently has been unable to develop, and hence the disrupting channel would eventually be no longer able to interfere with his speech.

It is now generally agreed among behaviour therapists that this technique does not produce satisfactory clinical results. That is, it does not transfer to real life situations. For various reasons I am not satisfied that this has been adequately demonstrated — I do not think the appropriate experiments have yet been done — but I will come back to that point in a minute.

121

An alternative procedure, which has been used more recently,[4] and which is a modification of a very old method, is that of using a metronome to pace the speech of the stutterer. You discover the optimal metronome beat at which the stutterer can emit word units — artificially, of course — without breaking down on them. This rate will vary very considerably from one stutterer to another. You then build such an apparatus in a hearing aid (as was mentioned this morning) which the stutterer carries around with him, and whenever he thinks he is going to stutter, he turns it on and uses it. It has been found, in a fair proportion of cases, though by no means uniformly so, that not only can stutterers use this apparatus and speak without stuttering, though initially of course in a somewhat artificial manner, but that they can gradually dispense with the unit, and make their speech more normal.

This raises the interesting question of why the metronome technique appears to work more satisfactorily than the shadowing technique. The answer, I think, is an important one. It is that the use of the metronome technique enables the stutterer to practise his non-stuttering speech in a real situation, whereas the shadowing technique has so far only been used in a laboratory. In other words we are back to the problem which has pervaded this symposium to some extent, that in order for these techniques to work they must be transferred somehow or other to the real life situation. My guess is that if, for instance, one were to construct a white noise apparatus which inhibits stuttering, and build this into a hearing aid which allowed the subject to carry it around with him, the results would be the same as for the metronome.

So this is one approach to the inhibition of stuttering and its transfer to real life. However, an approach which is really rather different, and as important as, if not more important than, the Cherry and Sayers techniques, is the outstanding work recently carried out by Israel Goldiamond[5] in the United States. Goldiamond is one of the most controversial of the operant conditioners in the United States, but there is no question of his genius and I think one can use the word quite advisedly. What the operant conditioners argue fundamentally, of course, is that behaviour — and speech is an example of behaviour — is controlled by its consequences on the environment. So if you manipulate the immediate consequences which follow the emission of speech units, either in an aversive or reinforcing manner, you can change the form of speech. This is precisely what Goldiamond and his colleagues have tried to do.

What they have shown is that you can control the fluency or non-fluency of normal speech by manipulating its consequences quite deliberately. Essentially what they do is to arrange for a particular unit of fluent or non-fluent speech either to produce, on the one hand, an aversive consequence, or on the other hand to turn off or eliminate an aversive consequence which is already present. Now let us see in more detail exactly how this works out, because it's rather complicated. We have the possibility of fluency or non-fluency units of speech. If a fluent unit of speech is followed — and this is arranged by the experimenter of course — by an aversive stimulus, then the subject will tend to become more non-fluent. If you like to use other terminology, what you're doing is punishing fluent speech. On the other hand, if fluent speech produces the offset or cessation of an aversive stimulus, then there will be a fluency increase. Similarly, in the case of non-fluent speech, if the non-fluent speech leads to the onset of an aversive stimulus, then the subject will tend to increase his fluency. Similarly, if non-fluency leads to the offset of an aversive stimulus, you will get a non-fluency increase.

Goldiamond, of course, like all operant conditioners, defines his aversive stimuli and his reinforcing stimuli operationally, that is, empirically. He is not interested in theory. By means of other experiments, he has empirically determined that an aversive stimulus which will control fluency of speech is a burst of high intensity white noise, whereas the cessation of a burst of high intensity white noise is a reinforcing situation. He has shown for each of these conditions that the predicted consequences will apply, that is, if the subject is speaking fluently and you punish him for it — give him an aversive stimulus — he will tend to become non-fluent; if, on the other hand, the aversive stimulus is present, and fluency turns it off, then the subject will increase his fluency. So far so good. However, Goldiamond also proposed to use delayed auditory feedback as an aversive stimulus, and its cessation or offset as a reinforcing stimulus. He has in fact reinterpreted the effects of delayed auditory feedback on normal speech as an aversive situation, that is, the reinforcing situation for normal speech is the normal delay in feedback of one millisecond. Delayed feedback is an aversive situation because it produces a situation in which expected feedback, which is reinforcing, is not received.

Goldiamond predicted that using delayed auditory feedback in these ways would produce exactly the same results. And so it did. Again, so far so good. Of course, precisely the same argument can be applied to stuttering. If stuttering is essentially a form of non-fluency, then manipulating the consequences of this non-fluency, either aversively or reinforcingly, will change the rate of emission of non-fluency. But what he found was that in the situation in which non-fluency, that is, stuttering, turned off delayed auditory feedback, and where one would expect a non-fluency increase — that is, he is arguing that you can actually increase the rate of stuttering, in stutterers, by this means — he did not, in fact, find it. What he found was that in this condition the stutter decreased. He did not find, however, that the decrease in stuttering produced normal speech, or fluent speech. What it produced was a cessation of stuttering, the exact opposite of the prediction, though this does not worry Goldiamond, because he is a pure empiricist. He simply accepts this result, without worrying about what it means.

It certainly worries me, but I think I know what the explanation is. I think it is a fairly straightforward though a complex explanation. Goldiamond just accepts it — this is one of his outstanding traits, the ability to seize on an empirical finding like this, and make use of it. What happened here was that the stutterer stopped stuttering, rather than increased stuttering, as predicted, but he also changed the form of his speech, and became like the ordinary subject, who responds to delayed auditory feedback by prolonging his speech. Remember I said that one way of overcoming the effects of delayed auditory feedback on speech in normal subjects is to stretch out speech. And this is precisely what the stutterer did, in this situation. As I said, this is contrary to what would be predicted on the basis of his white noise as an aversive stimulus, and of all the other results with delayed auditory feedback with stutterers.

But what he then did was the really important part. He said, "Right, what we've done is to eliminate the stuttering, that's vanished. We have now, in the original stutterer, a new form of speech, which is not normal speech, but which certainly is not stuttering. Let us now shape this new form of speech into normal speech." In other words, the main difference between normal speech and this prolongation is simply the time variable, that is, the stretching out of the speech, otherwise it is very similar to normal speech. The way in which he did this was first of all to start speeding up this new form of speech by getting the subject to read under the condition which produced the altered speech with the use of a perceptoscope. A perceptoscope is simply a piece of apparatus which enables you to vary the rate at which verbal material is presented to the subject. In this way, he began to force the subject to increase his reading rate. At the same time, he began to eliminate the delayed auditory feedback which had produced this change in speech.

In other words, what he was trying to do was this. He had brought the stutterer's speech under external control and he was now beginning to manipulate the external control in such a way that he could gradually shift the controlling stimuli which would now produce the new form of speech. And he found that by using these techniques he could gradually eliminate the delayed auditory feedback, maintain the new form of speech, and speed it up to the point where the subject's speech was as fluent as normal speech, and indistinguishable from it. In other words, he gradually telescoped these prolongations. But this was not all. What Goldiamond has done in addition to this is to say one further thing. And I think that this is one of the most crucial developments in behaviour therapy which must take place, but which has not yet taken place, except in these few instances. He said: "What we have done is essentially to control the external contingencies which maintain speech. But this is not good enough, because we are still essentially in an artificial situation. What we must do now is to gradually shift the contingencies controlling this new form of speech and change them, so that speech comes under the more normal contingency controls which maintain speech in normal subjects." And essentially what he has gone on to do is to extend this technique to produce normal speech more and more in situations which approximate real situations.

In fact, he has set up this situation so that the subject can carry around the delayed auditory feedback apparatus with him, in exactly the same way as Meyer's patients carried around a metronome. So that essentially his major contribution is to show how you can shift or how you can begin to shift from the artificial laboratory type of external control of a particular piece of behaviour, and produce what he calls self-control, that is, internalized control. And it is interesting to note that in this very long paper, which gives many more details than I've been able to, he talks about the subject becoming his own experimenter. He actually eventually sets up a dialogue between the experimenter and the subject to find out what are the situations in which he has stuttered in the past, to discuss ways in which he can learn to control his speech, and thereby to shift the contingencies from the control of the experimenter to the control of the subject.

What he is trying to do is to take this initial method out of the laboratory and into real life by modifying it appropriately. Now in part this involves putting the subject into situations which more and more approximate real life, such as getting him to take part in plays and other kinds of interactions with other people. As I said, it is quite clear now that for these kinds of techniques to be successful, at one stage or another one must go out of the laboratory and into real life, because that is where behaviour is performed. But I would not agree with previous speakers who argue that that is where you should start, taking as an analogy the engineer, who does not build bridges in his laboratory but goes out into the field. Even he does his basic experiments within the laboratory. And I think that the proper way of doing this work is to start in the laboratory, because that is where you can meaningfully bring the behaviour under experimental control. At some time or other, however, you are faced with the problem of shifting gradually into real life, and it is this aspect that I think Goldiamond has so ingeniously achieved.

REFERENCES

1. Yates, A.J. (1963). Delayed auditory feedback. *Psychol. Bull.* **60,** 213-32.
2. Yates, A.J. (1963). Recent empirical and theoretical approaches to the experimental manipulation of speech in normal subjects and in stammerers. *Behav. Res. Ther.* **1,** 95-119.
3. Cherry, C. & Sayers, B. McA. (1956). Experiments upon the total inhibition of stammering by external control and some clinical results. *J. psychosom. Res.* **1,** 233-46.
4. Meyer, V. & Mair, J.M.M. (1963). A new technique to control stammering: a preliminary report. *Behav. Res. Ther.* **1,** 251-54.
5. Goldiamond, I. (1965). Stuttering and fluency as manipulatable operant response classes. In *Research in behaviour modification* (ed. L. Krasner & L.P. Ullmann), pp. 106-56. New York: Holt.

SEMINAR FOUR: PAPER FOUR
Research in Behaviour Therapy

Dr. G. L. Mangan

Let me begin by making a general comment. I am not completely in accord with the position adopted by Lovibond, that behavioural modification rests on a standardized set of procedures, that with the monosymptomatic disorders it is relatively simple to select equivalent groups, nor am I at ease with the more esoteric view of Yates, that each patient is a separate problem, which precludes the possibility of standard batteries of techniques in the foreseeable future. I find myself settled between these two points of view.

This consideration applies especially to the first set of research issues I intend to raise, which, incidentally, has been touched on by a number of speakers, viz. the mechanics of developing techniques, and the contexts in which they occur.

The second set of issues may appear to be somewhat academic and remote. I might refer to them appropriately as "pure" research. However, I think these might in the future provide us with data — and the insight deriving from the interpretation of such data — useful in the development of a comprehensive behaviour theory, which could direct the development of our skills of influence and modification.

THE MECHANICS OF DEVELOPING TECHNIQUES

Here one can identify at least two major issues, the first relating to the utilization of interview skills, which comes under the broad heading of verbal conditioning, the second to the development of more rigidly controlled laboratory conditioning techniques and operations.

127

The traditional psychotherapies utilize indirect, verbal methods to modify behaviour. The cost of interview therapy (Schofield[1] describes dynamic interview relationships as "purchasable friendship") and their relative ineffectiveness, however, have led to intensified efforts to develop new techniques, largely experimental. Unfortunately, disenchantment with the traditional methods has led in some quarters to an uncritical abandonment of interview therapy in toto.

It is clear, however, that direct verbal suggestion can affect the learning process in therapy. Research has shown that conditioning of verbal behaviour does occur in a systematic way during psychotherapy, and that this has consequences in other behaviour. The skills and insights derived from interview therapy can be utilized, although the exact nature of the influence, and the conditions under which this can be maximized, require precise determination. It is possible that, for example, efficient verbal conditioning may be all that is necessary to deal with the confused but fairly socially adequate person, who now, under the aegis of behaviour therapy, is treated by techniques such as "assertive training" which, if we can accept Wolpe and Lazarus' description,[2] appears to be basically a combination of oneupmanship and the power of positive thinking.

One is reminded here also of the so-called verbal aversion technique.[3] In the treatment of alcoholics, for example, drug-induced nausea is reinforced both by verbal suggestions that the patient is sick, that the to-be-modified behaviour should be avoided, and by the sound of vomiting. Oswald comments favourably on the efficacy of such aversive verbal conditioning in conjunction with the aversive drug technique.

From the extensive literature of behaviour therapy, however, it is clear that many patients are best served by one of the many non-verbal conditioning procedures. But if one is committed to this goal, one faces then the formidable task of efficiently matching patients to treatments.

Unfortunately, research along these lines has been rather indifferent; such elementary problems as, for example, the selection of efficient experimental designs for use with individual cases have not been adequately treated, although we all recognize that the ultimate utility of most forms of behaviour therapy lies with the individual case. How much control is necessary over the patient's physical and social environment? What are the specific responses to be selected for treatment, and what are the appropriate reinforcement schedules and reinforcing stimuli during the course of treatment? Our lack of information on these and other equally important variables reflects the primitive state of our current repertoire of conditioning techniques.

In constructing reliable and valid therapeutic techniques and procedures, we should aim at a methodological sophistication similar to that attained in the design of psychological tests and laboratory experiments, systematically manipulating and measuring all the restricting and facilitating conditions which apply in conditioning generally. Simple conditioning is not as simple as it is made out to be. This is a basic requirement before we can hope to achieve — if we consider this to be a legitimate goal — sets of programmes available to the therapist, who can select treatment schedules for use on a patient to accomplish a predictable goal.

In addition, of course, considerable research is necessary on the development of the less well-known and well-tried techniques — anxiety relief technique, flooding technique, thought stopping and abreaction techniques, and on the most effective combinations of these — for example the aversive treatment-anxiety relief combination in the treatment of homosexuality, generating both approach to heterosexual and avoidance of homosexual tendencies. The very scanty treatment of these techniques in the latest Wolpe and Lazarus book points to the necessity for objective evaluation of this sort.

"PURE" RESEARCH AREAS

I mentioned at the beginning of this paper that the second set of issues I intended to raise were somewhat academic, but that I thought some of them might in the long term provide a basis for a more comprehensive behaviour theory, out of which more efficient modification techniques might develop. From the tremendous flux of ongoing work, I have selected four problems which I think are both interesting and critical. These concern certain aspects of verbal conditioning, the problem of individual differences in higher nervous activity, and the relationship of these to a factor of "conditionability", the problem of control of "involuntary" processes, and the problem of muscle tension utilization. Superficially, at least, these show little overlap, so the remainder of this paper might appear somewhat fragmentary.

It comes as a matter of some surprise to realize how little interest is engendered by the Russian conditioning therapy approach, utilizing techniques of suggestion and hypnosis. Studies have reported roughly the same percentage of complete and partial improvement as Wolpe and Lazarus, using different conditioning techniques, but a faster rate of remission. For example, Platonov, in his book *The Word as a Physiological and Therapeutic Factor*[4] reports cases in which severe symptoms are removed in six–ten sessions of verbal conditioning or reconditioning under suggested sleep followed by suggested rest, compared with twenty–thirty sessions required in roughly similar cases where treatment is systematic desensitization using reciprocal inhibition. Gordova and Kovalev,[5] in a study dealing with aversion treatment of chronic alcholics, report that hypnosis is as effective as hypnosis plus apomorphine, both treatments being significantly superior to apomorphine alone.

Apart from prejudice, the main reason for our mistrust of such procedures lies in the fact that although we do not today conceive of suggestion and hypnosis as occult entities, these are still areas which involve mysticism, controversy and discontinuity with "normal" behaviour, harking back to the notion of a relationship between hypnotizability and suggestibility and hysteria, deriving initially from Charcot. Even with those investigators such as Sarbin[6] and Barber,[7] who view hypnotic phenomena as normal behaviour under particular conditions, hypnosis is viewed simply as role enactment, and the value of hypnosis as a therapeutic tool is considered to be small.

Russian theorists, however, conceptualize suggestion and hypnosis, which are central in their theories of conditioning therapy, in a very different way. In order to appreciate their theorizing, I think it necessary to consider a number of general theoretical propositions which provide the framework in which these conceptualizations occur. Let me detail the most important of these.

a) Bykov has demonstrated the possibility of conditioned reflex relations with all internal organs and systems. Thus the entire internal environment is considered to be subject to the influence of the cortex.

b) In humans, there is an addendum to the laws governing higher nervous activity in animals. This involves the speech function, introducing a new principle into the activity of the cortex, a second signal system typical only of man. Words can become CSs.

c) Conditioned reflexes of the second signal system are formed on the material basis of the first signal system, and act on both the first signal system and on subcortical structures. Words influence the second signal system, and through it, the first signal system and the subcortical structures.

The nature of sleep, suggestion and hypnosis have been elaborated in this general context. Sleep is spreading inhibition, due to the accumulation of metabolites, or functional exhaustion of the cortical cells. Active sleep is inhibition of the whole cortex and the subcortical structures, while passive sleep, which can be produced by stroking, weak, monotonous stimulation, restriction of movement or verbal suggestion and is facilitated by fatigue, a weak type of nervous system, or strong negative emotion, produces inhibition in cortical cells which spreads gradually over the cortex. Conditioned reflex sleep can be produced without exhaustion.

According to Pavlov, sleep inhibition can be partial in depth and extensiveness, and can develop in restricted regions of the cortex. One part of the cortex may be inhibited, the other awake or excited. It is interesting to note that this phenomenon of differential excitability in the cortex has also been proposed by Oswald.[8] The waking section of the cortex, which Pavlov called the sentry post in the first signal (i.e. sensory) system, the "rapport" zone in the second signal (i.e. verbal) system, may be in a state of increased excitability, due to the surrounding inhibition. As the excitability of the wakeful section becomes relatively greater, verbal suggestion becomes more and more effective. The opportunity for reconditioning under these conditions is considerably improved.

This is the theory underlying Russian verbal conditioning. We, however, struggle with a mélange of learning theories, probably settling for a mixed grill of Hull and Osgood, garnished with Spence and Estes. These theories, however, tend to ignore the learning potential conferred by a much more complex, elaborate and highly developed cortex, with its second signal system of reality, and its great potential for verbal conditioning.

I am not advocating a return to the nineteenth century suggestion therapy of Bernheim, though I shall probably be accused of this. Nor am I suggesting uncritical acceptance of all Pavlovian and neo-Pavlovian postulates. What I am suggesting is that to our own learning constructs we add and exploit the constructs of Pavlov, Bykov, Anokhin and others, particularly those relating to verbal and interoceptive conditioning. One tends to despair a little however, when one sees the oversimplified way in which Pavlov is normally treated (e.g. by Eysenck) and the fate of theorists and empiricists such as Razran and Gantt, who have tried, with singular lack of success, to wed Pavlovian and neo-Pavlovian constructs to Western learning theory.

In discussing the Pavlovian suggestibility concept, I mentioned that type of nervous system is important. This brings me to my second issue. According to Pavlov,[9] individuals differ in the strength of the excitatory and inhibitory processes, their mobility

— the ease of switching from excitation to inhibition and vice versa — and their balance. I am not concerned with the validity of these typological constructs in relation to the etiological problems in neurosis, although Pavlov considered neurosis to be due to a sharp imbalance or derangement of higher nervous activity. I am concerned, however, with their validity insofar as general conditionability is concerned. In the West, researchers such as Eysenck, Franks, Spence, and Lovibond have attempted to isolate a general factor of conditionability, and to determine its relation to personality dimensions such as extraversion and neuroticism. On the whole, attempts have been unsuccessful, but there are some indications that there may be nervous system characteristics which relate to conditioning performance.

Whereas Pavlov considered that weakness/strength of the nervous system was determined by the amount of excitatory substances in the cortical cells, and that this was related to conditioning performance, Teplov and Nebylitsyn[10] have theorized that the reactivity of the excitatory substances is the critical element. They have postulated a dimension of sensitivity — strength; the sensitive (weak in Pavlov's terms) system has a lower absolute threshold than the strong system; it also has a lower threshold of transmarginal or protective inhibition, i.e. the stimulus intensity at which the cells cease responding as a protection against damage. There are also indications that a high neuroticism score is associated with a lower threshold of protective inhibition.

Thus, according to Nebylitsyn,[11] the range of stimulation to which all subjects respond is the same. In the sensitive system, however, a moderate stimulus elicits a larger amplitude response, because of the relatively stronger focus of excitation in the sensitive cortex, while to the strong system, the stimulus is relatively weak, producing a weak focus of excitation, and thus response.

The concept of differential sensitivity to stimuli is critical for conditioning generally, and may be particularly relevant to optimal levels of stimulation in aversive conditioning. Since stimuli normally obey the law of strength, relating stimulus intensity to response magnitude, CS and UCS intensity should be a constant above-threshold value for all subjects.

The concept of transmarginal inhibition is unfamiliar to most Western theorists, though there are some reports of a similar type of inhibitory effect. Venables and Tizard,[12] for example, report that schizophrenics show a decrement in reaction time to a significantly less intense stimulus than normals, a finding which, incidentally, accords with the Russian view that schizophrenics have a lower threshold of protective inhibition than normals.

Apart from such instances, however, the concept has been accorded scant attention, though the similarity of this conceptualization to the well-known inverted U relationship between arousal and performance is obvious enough. It might be that something like protective inhibition accounts for the observation that at times strong stimuli evoke weak responses — for example, that some practising homosexuals are less aroused by a "strong" stimulus (picture of a nude male in a sexually suggestive position) than by a "moderate" stimulus (picture of a clothed male).

We need to know a good deal more about these phenomena, about their relation to conditioning parameters, to personality dimensions such as extraversion and neuroticism, and to certain aspects of behavioural abnormality. Failure to consider these phenomena may have contributed in part to the lack of success in identifying a "conditionability" factor. In any event, if nothing more such consideration may bring into closer reciprocal relationship the large body of Russian conditioning data with Western personality research. This in itself seems to me a worth-while research goal.

A third problem which has excited increasing interest over the past few years, and one which has considerable significance for clinical research, is the question of control of "involuntary" processes. To what extent are processes normally considered outside a subject's voluntary control — vasomotor responses, heart rate, GSR and so on — controllable by the subject, and, if so, under what conditions? Interest in this problem derives initially from Russian work, although the problem has been touched on by American investigators, somewhat hesitantly, since certain basic assumptions tend to violate the *zeitgeist*.

It seems clear from a number of studies that control of "involuntary" processes requires artificial feedback of one sort or another. Lisina[13] reports that subjects were able to change from vasoconstriction to vasodilation to terminate shock, but only after becoming aware, through visual feedback, of the reinforcing value of vasodilation. The sham studies of Ayrepetyants[14] indicate that subjects can experience an irresistible urge to urinate when the bladder is empty. After subjects had learnt the connection between dial readings and interoceptive stimuli signalling distension of the bladder, Ayrepetyants reversed the dial readings and reported that subjects now experienced the irresistible urge when in fact the bladder was empty, providing the dial reading indicated (falsely) that the bladder was full. The work of Basmajian[15] demonstrating the ability of some subjects to initiate the firing of single motor neurons with the use of feedback, and a number of

133

studies on heart rate control using feedback, all point to the proposition that many responses up till now considered involuntary can be brought under control by some subjects under certain conditions.

It is indeed tempting to infer that such control is "conscious" or "cognitive" control. The problem seems somewhat less simple than this, however, since there are indications from some studies that when a subject is unaware of the connection between the exteroceptive signal and some internal state of affairs, control is more quickly achieved.

A further step is that of substitution of self-produced verbal stimuli for the feedback stimuli, thus bringing the response more under the subject's immediate control by removing it from stimulus contingencies in the environment. The possibility of such substitution has been clearly demonstrated.

The significance of this kind of work seems to me obvious and exciting. For example, it may have particular application to the problem of pervasive anxiety, where the anxiety is usually not under detectable stimulus control. However, we need to know precisely what response classes are amenable to control, the most appropriate feedback procedures to maximize such control, and whether personality factors are related to control variables, to name a few of the problems which come immediately to mind.

The fourth area involves the dynamic role of muscle tension in defending the organism against anxiety. Such a possibility is either implicitly or explicitly indicated in the theorizing of Freud, Jung, Ferenczi, of Braatoy in his treatment of hysterical conversions, and of modern analytically oriented therapists such as Shatan and Christensen, to name a few. It is generally proposed that the relaxation of muscular rigidity liberates effective energy, and restores to memory the situation in which the repression occurred. Thus the release of muscle tension is accompanied by the release of lively memories related to the situation or conflict that originally created the muscle tension.

Clinical evidence in part supports this proposition. Hefferline[16] reports that when a chronic muscle tension is reduced there is often an accompanying vivid spontaneous recall of typical situations in which the subject learnt to be tense in this particular manner. The same phenomenon is reported by Malmo and Braatoy, both of whom additionally investigated the relationship of the thematic content of recall and the localization of the tension. Braatoy found that release of chronic paralyses of the arm was accompanied by feelings of aggression towards the father, Malmo that tension in the thigh muscles is associated with sexual conflict.

134

There is an obvious contradiction here. At the basis of Wolpe's desensitization procedures, and in accord with common sense, relaxation is an antagonist of anxiety responses. I cannot suggest any reason for this contradiction. Perhaps it lies in the different amounts of relaxation induced. Whatever the case, however, the problem is an interesting one, since it suggests, amongst other things, that here we may have a method of producing abreaction, which is suggested as a useful technique by Wolpe and Lazarus. Incidentally, the emergence of this problem points up the barrenness of uncritical, outright rejection of dynamic postulates and observations.

In conclusion, I am constrained to point out that the issues I have touched on are only a few of the many. And although I stated originally that there appeared to be little overlap between these problem areas, it is worth mentioning that some relationships — admittedly tenuous — appear to be emerging. For example, some recent work indicates that variables relevant to both control of involuntary processes and muscle tension utilization are related to personality dimensions. While one would hesitate at this stage to predict highly significant relationships between personality variables such as barrier penetration, field dependence, extraversion and so on, and psychophysiological variables such as "sensitivity" of the nervous system, "sensitivity" to feedback from the striate musculature, which, in turn, might have reference to "conditionability", such relationships are plausible, and perhaps simply wait exposure by further research.

REFERENCES

1. Schofield, W. (1964). *Psychotherapy: the purchase of friendship*. Englewood Cliffs, N.J.: Prentice-Hall.
2. Wolpe, J. & Lazarus, A.A. (1966). *Behaviour therapy techniques*. London: Pergamon.
3. Oswald, I. (1962). Introduction of illusory and hallucinatory voices with considerations of behaviour therapy. *J. ment. Sci.* **108**, 196-212.
4. Platonov, K. (1959). *The word as a physiological and therapeutic factor*. Moscow: Foreign Languages Publishing House.
5. Gordova & Kovalev (1966). Cited by B.H. Kirman, Psychotherapy in the Soviet Union. In *Present-day Russian psychology* (ed. N. O'Connor), p. 42. London: Pergamon.
6. Sarbin, T.R. (1965). Hypnosis as a behaviour modification technique. In *Research in behaviour modification* (ed. L. Krasner & L.P. Ullmann). New York: Holt, Rinehart and Winston.
7. Barber, T.X. (1964) Hypnotizability, suggestibility and personality. V. A critical review of research findings. *Psychol. Rep.* **14**, 299-320.
8. Oswald, I. (1962). *Sleeping and waking: physiology and psychology*. London: Elsevier.
9. Pavlov, I.P. (1955). *Selected works* (Translated by S. Belsky), pp. 315-44. Moscow: Foreign Languages Publishing House.

10. Teplov, B.M. & Nebylitsyn, V.D. (1966). Results of experimental studies on properties of the nervous system in man. In *Psychological research in the U.S.S.R.* (ed. A. Leontiev, A. Luria & A. Smirnov), vol. 1, pp. 181-98. Moscow: Progress Publishers.
11. Nebylitsyn, V.D. (1959). An investigation of the connection between sensitivity and strength of the nervous system. In *Tipologicheskiye osobennosti vysshei nervnoi deyatelnosti cheloveka* (ed. B.M. Teplov), vol. 2, 1959, pp. 48-82. English translation by J.A. Gray in *Pavlov's typology* (ed. J.A. Gray), pp. 402-45. Oxford: Pergamon, 1964.
12. Venables, P.H. & Tizard, J. (1956). Paradoxical effects in the reaction time of schizophrenics. *J. abnorm. soc. Psychol.* **53**, 220-24.
13. Lisina, M.I. (1961). The role of orientation in the transformation of involuntary reactions into voluntary ones. Cited by G. Razran, in The observable unconscious and the inferable conscious in current Soviet psychophysiology: interoceptive conditioning, semantic conditioning and the orienting reflex. *Psychol. Rev.* **68**, 81-147.
14. Ayrepetyants, E. Sh. (1956). Materials on the internal analyser in man. *Trudy Inst. Fiziol. I.P. Pavlova* **5**, 396-406 (English translation).
15. Basmajian, J.V. (1963). Conscious control of single nerve cells. *New Scient.* **20**, 662-64.
16. Hefferline, R.F. (1958). The role of proprioception in the control of behaviour. *Trans. N.Y. Acad. Sci.* **20**, 739-64.

RECAPITULATION

RECAPITULATION

Dr. S. H. Lovibond and
Professor A. J. Yates

DR. LOVIBOND

It seems to me that it is rather fruitless for two of us to attempt to do what Professor Hammer did yesterday, and it occurs to me that I'm possibly taking this term recapitulation too literally. Perhaps the term was put there as a polite way of giving Professor Yates and myself the chance of having the last say. So I'm going to interpret it that way but I'm not going to attempt, as it were, to pull together all the strings as I see them. What I want to do is to take out just one or two points that have emerged either from the discussion during the course of the papers or in private discussion.

The first point I want to take up is this one of what becomes the conditioned stimulus. You will remember that this problem arose in the discussion of the boy who interfered with horses. This is a very important practical issue, and it is an issue on which there appears to be rather liberal empirical evidence. Some time ago, I came to the conclusion that from the evidence there is available it seems reasonable to draw a conclusion that what is likely, or more likely, to become a CS is the stimulus change that immediately precedes the point of reinforcement. Wolpe has argued that, appearances notwithstanding, even pervasive anxiety is under stimulus control, and that if you search assiduously enough you will be able to discover the stimuli that control the anxiety. Because the anxiety is highly generalized, occurs widely and seems to be present pretty well all the time, this is simply an indication that the CSs eliciting it are stimuli which are present most of the time. He just rolls off one or two examples such as the awareness of one's own body, differences in light and shade, things of this nature, passage of time and so on.

It seems to me that this is entirely implausible, that under ordinary circumstances you would not expect background stimulation of this sort to become part of the stimulus complex, unless there was no change in the stimulus situation which could in fact become more readily the CS. Recently, there has been some direct experimental work on this, and in Prokasy's *Classical Conditioning*[1] there is a chapter by Leo Kamin of McMaster University in which he has taken up this issue, from a quite different point of view of course, but he has shown that in the conditioned emotional response, for example, what happens is that you teach an animal — a rat — to press a bar for food at a steady rate, and then you superimpose on this bar-pressing a CS, which in Kamin's procedure lasts for three minutes, and follow it up with an electric shock. After a time Kamin found that presentation of this CS, a tone, would itself suppress the bar-pressing.

What Kamin has explored is the effect of complex stimuli, complex in the sense that there are a number of components. If you break this complex up into 180 seconds, or a minute and a half of tone followed by a minute and a half of light, then the tone has practically no depressant effect at all. All the depressant effect is associated with the light. This seems to me to suggest that the general conclusion is not far out. And so I think this has a certain practical application, and can be applied to the kind of situation we were talking about yesterday.

I just want to say a few words about this issue of individual control versus application of general principles. Thinking about this a little further, it seems to me that Professor Yates would probably agree that ultimately our aim is to develop a set of principles which will have wide applicability. But when you come down to applying any sorts of behavioural principles, in a concrete case of course, you are faced with the sort of situation which I tried to describe yesterday, where it is necessary to make a large number of decisions on the basis of quite inadequate evidence. In other words, there just isn't sufficient information to guide you in your choice of stimulus parameters, for example, at different points, and it is not possible to take the necessary time off to plan the steps on which to base your decision. And perhaps what you do is exercise your clinical judgment; you do exactly the same as any other clinician. You have to make judgments about what is the most efficacious, or likely to be the most efficacious, procedure. It seems to me that by the very nature of things it must always be like this because general principles represent abstractions from

140

concrete situations, and, in order to apply them, we've got to give them concrete content. And that sort of situation must necessarily continue to apply.

On this question, Professor Yates and one or two others seemed to fear the institutionalization of present techniques. I cannot see the basis for this really, because if this is what's happening, if you take aversion therapy, for example, there is an enormous variation in procedure from one clinician to another. If you look in the pages of the journals — *Behaviour Research and Therapy,* for example — you will see in almost every issue that people are bringing out new techniques, and that the problem is that most of them are not sufficiently validated. People are attempting to introduce new techniques before the old ones have been sufficiently tested. Furthermore, in relation to reciprocal inhibition, far from this becoming a standardized set of procedures which everyone accepts as having unquestioned validity, now there are all sorts of experimental analyses of the features of the situation which produce the therapeutic effects. So I suppose I'm naturally a lot more optimistic. I don't agree with Professor Yates that we can't hope to get anything approaching an adequate comprehensive behaviour theory which will guide practice rather better than anything we have at the moment, for fifty or a hundred years.

I have this distressing feeling that all along I've been dodging an issue that Professor Hammer raised. He's cornered me on odd occasions and asked me to justify myself. I can't do so — I can't answer the sorts of queries he's raising. It has to do with this issue of continuity-noncontinuity, or, as Dr. McConaghy phrased it this morning, whether at a certain point there is a change to pathological states, in which the laws of behaviour maintenance and modification, or the laws of nervous functioning, if you like to look at it in the Pavlovian sense, in fact become different. Now I implied yesterday that I believe that this is most likely to be the case. Here I part company with the majority of behaviour therapists because it is a cardinal assumption of most people who engage in behaviour therapy that there is a complete continuity between normal and abnormal behaviour. This is put very nicely in an article by Sidman entitled "Normal sources of pathological behaviour". He makes the principles absolutely explicit and goes on to show how apparently abnormal behaviour in animals can be derived from quite normal principles of behavioural acquisition. Most Western writers refuse to believe that Pavlov established a disordered nervous state when the animal was made experimentally neurotic. I've found some very distorted attempts to explain the behavioural manifestations in terms of straightforward acquisition of conditioned linkages.

I would re-emphasize what I said yesterday. I'm fully aware that this assumption of mine that there is discontinuity is not parsimonious and I can see very well the strength of the argument of people who maintain that until you can show that this leads to consequences of some importance that can't be derived from the more parsimonious point of view, then they won't be interested. I am fully aware that if I want to get people to accept this idea I've got to produce some evidence that it has consequences for experiment and practice that the continuity point of view doesn't have. I can't answer these questions that Professor Hammer raises, but I have a great deal of sympathy for him when he asserts that they are ones that have to be faced.

Now I was going to say a little about the question of individual differences that Dr. Mangan raised, but I think I'll just close with a very small point. Dr. McConaghy seemed to think that there was some sort of contradiction between his reading of the literature and his understanding of the viewpoint of Western behaviourists in relation to Pavlovian theory and findings and Dr. Mangan's views. He seemed to think that the position wasn't quite as bad in terms of lack of communication of knowledge as Mangan maintains. It seems to me that the difference is that Mangan was talking about physiological psychologists whereas McConaghy is talking about neurophysiologists. In fact the interest of Western neurophysiologists in Pavlovian theories can easily be checked by picking up any issue of a journal such as *EEG and Clinical Neurophysiology*. There is now a tremendous interest and a new respect for this theory, whereas only ten or fifteen years ago there was a tendency to reject it out of hand.

PROFESSOR YATES

It is customary on occasions like this to say that a symposium of this kind has been very valuable and one has learnt all sorts of things from it. I want to say this quite genuinely on this occasion, because I have discovered some very interesting things that I wasn't aware of before, and I think some of the most important issues have been formulated quite clearly. Differences of opinion about some of these have been made quite clear, even if they haven't been resolved. I just want to mention a few of these.

Firstly, I was somewhat surprised to find the rather wide divergence of views by those of us here who would accept being called behaviour therapists — some of us might prefer to be called behaviour modifiers — about the basic nature of behaviour therapy. My own view is that behaviour therapy involves dealing with the clinical case on an experimental basis. I haven't quite discovered how I'm supposed to differ from Professor Hammer. I suspect that the only difference is in the kinds of theoretical constructs which we use, and I suspect that when it comes down to the point of actually dealing with a similar case, the kinds of operations that he indulges in would not be very different from the kinds of operations I would indulge in. The difference between myself and Dr. McConaghy would be rather more fundamental, because Dr. McConaghy seems to be saying that at the present time it is inefficient to try to carry out experiments on the single case, and that we would get ahead faster if we did the kinds of experiments that he reported in his paper.

I want to make it quite clear that I have no objections whatever to the kinds of experiment that Dr. McConaghy reported but I would not regard these as being primarily behaviour therapy as I understand it, rather as prolegomena to behaviour therapy, and I would hope that when the kinds of experiments that he described to us have been carried much further, and he is faced with a single case that comes up to him and says "I want my sexual behaviour changed from homosexual to heterosexual", he would not then simply, in a standard fashion, apply a standard technique. Rather that however much information he has gathered from these experiments, he will regard this particular patient as a problem in his own right. And I'm quite certain, as I think I was able to demonstrate in Goldiamond's case, that given the diversity os human behaviour, it is most unlikely that however many principlef we might evolve, and whatever knowledge we have, we will ever be able to devise a set of purely standard techniques of the kind that Dr. Mangan talked about.

Dr. Lovibond, on the other hand, if I understood him correctly, tends to understress the value of theory in behaviour therapy at the present time, and to regard our efforts as more of a technological nature. That is, we try to do what we can with what we have. Now I don't think that the differences between the various speakers that I've mentioned are very important, because I think we're all going along in the same direction towards the same goals at somewhat different levels. In Dr. Lovibond's case, however, what impressed me was not the fact that the child got better; I still think it possible that the child got better for reasons other than those connected with what Dr. Lovibond did, and I think it would be fatal to assume that what Dr. Lovibond did necessarily had anything to do with the results that he obtained. I think we've had too many false positives in the past, as it were, to be confident of that. My own experience in the treatment of tics, which I reported to you, shows how cautious one must be. What impressed me about Dr. Lovibond's paper was — I'm tempted to call it theory — the way in which he looked at the relevant experimental literature on aversive conditioning, and from that derived the principles or the methods which he actually used. This is what I think is important, because here he was clearly, in an individual case, trying to make use of relevant parts of that body of knowledge which we call psychology.

Another major achievement of his which indicates the interaction between theory and experiment or empirical knowledge is the way in which he was able to infer that one of the reasons for relapse rate in enuresis was the failure to use partial reinforcement techniques. It follows, we hope, from the literature on partial reinforcement that if we want to increase resistance to extinction, that is, maintain control over micturition, then we should use partial reinforcement techniques.

I must also make reference to the basic questions raised by Professor Hammer, which I also attempted to answer. There were three he particularly mentioned. The first was to what range of abnormal behaviour is behaviour therapy appropriate. Well, I think actually this is an illegitimate question. I don't think we know the answer, but if I had to give an answer, I would say that behaviour therapy is applicable to any form of behaviour. That's the simple answer. I wouldn't want to place any restriction on the kinds of behaviour to which the techniques and the theories of behaviour therapy may be applied.

The second question, which Dr. Lovibond touched on, is whether there is a qualitative difference in abnormal behaviour, or some forms of abnormal behaviour, as compared with normal behaviour. Here again, I think the answer can only be an empirical one, but I don't think that the undeniable differences between phobias that are found in some people and phobias that are found in others — to be more specific what we might call patient phobias and student phobias — necessarily imply that we should assume that we do need to introduce new principles. I have no doubt at all that the kinds of phobias that we find in hospitalized patients, for example, are different from the kinds of phobias that have often been dealt with — the so-called monosymptomatic phobias — by some behaviour therapists. But this merely means that the determination of the exact nature of the phobia is multidimensional, and that we must take into account the very large number of factors in arriving at an explanation of the particular kind of phobia that the person shows.

I could give a long lecture on this, and in fact I hope to do so at the next Australian Psychological Society conference. In distinguishing between different kinds of phobias and their amenability to treatment we have to make, for example, a distinction which I make now between neurotic behaviour and abnormal behaviour, because I do not believe that all forms of abnormal behaviour are neurotic behaviour, whereas one might argue that neurotic behaviour is abnormal. One also has to take into account the degree of stress to which the individual is exposed, and a large number of other factors which I hope to integrate, to account for the differences between kinds of phobias that are found in neurotic people and the kinds of phobias that are found in non-neurotic people. But this doesn't necessarily imply that there are any new principles specific to neurotic forms of behaviour; rather that the end form of the abnormal behaviour is determined by a large number of factors which have a differential importance in different circumstances. I'm sorry I can't go into more details, but as I said I'm trying to work this out at the present time.

The third point I think relates to the complexity of behaviour therapy. I think that I would argue that I have not come across, as yet, any form of abnormal behaviour which could be described as simple. I think that this misapprehension has arisen, as I've said before, from the fact that behaviour therapists have tended so far to deal with those kinds of abnormal behaviour which appear, on the surface, to be readily quantifiable and scorable, so that you can attempt to assess changes in behaviour as the result of the manipulation of different variables. But I'm quite convinced that, in the case of the more complex behavioural disturbances, you will have to formulate much more complex models to attempt to account for these disturbances and to ameliorate them. I referred yesterday, I think, to the increasingly great use of mediational constructs which will have to be made. We're merely on the threshold of discovery here. I don't think we will discover standard techniques for a very long time. I do think there is a danger that behaviour therapy is becoming institutionalized — here you have a disorder, and there a preferred method of treatment. Dr. Lovibond said that there were differences in systematic desensitization techniques. This is true of course, but the crucial point is that these differences are not themselves being properly explored, experimentally. In other words, what I'm saying is that we do not know more than a fraction of what we should know about systematic desensitization, and therefore we cannot apply this meaningfully in standard fashion. I agree entirely with Dr. Mangan about the restrictiveness of the kinds of models which we have used so far, and I have castigated the tendency to identify behaviour therapy with learning theory.

145

I myself feel that the Russian experimental work on internal conditioning and so on is fundamental. But I think that the so-called work in which they have tried to apply these notions to abnormal patients is so poor as to be simply not worth reading. In other words, I make a distinction between their strictly experimental work and their so-called clinical work on which I think Professor Hammer's strictures were perfectly justified.

Finally, I'd like to comment on the ethical problems of behaviour therapy with particular reference to Professor Whitlock's comments. It doesn't surprise me that what is sometimes called aversion therapy and sometimes by the more old-fashioned term punishment arouses a certain degree of worry and apprehension in psychiatrists and psychologists who have to do with patients. I think here in a sense we're being bemused by the use of a term, because no one here, in criticizing the use of punishment, has asked what we mean by the term. Anyone who has read Richard Solomon's recent summary paper on punishment will realize what an extraordinarily complex area this is. Professor Whitlock seemed to hint that giving electric shocks to patients in certain circumstances was punishing them. But is it? What exactly do we mean by punishing them? Is for example the use of ECT or electric shock therapy punishment? It's still used quite widely by psychiatrists. Is hospitalizing a patient in a mental hospital against his will a form of punishment? Is taking a patient through psychotherapy a form of punishment, because it indicates to him that he is a second class citizen when he is in psychotherapy?

Secondly, I'm wondering what the position would be of those people who are very worried about the use of aversion therapy, if the patient himself asks for this kind of therapy, after it has been explained to him. Would they prevent the treatment, would they instruct the psychologist not to employ such a treatment? Is it a matter of whether the patient wants it or not because he thinks it might work, or might help him? Perhaps he doesn't see the administration of electric shock as a punishing situation at all. After all, psychiatrists have been telling us for a long time that it is far better if you want to punish a child to punish him. Some psychiatrists say that if you're going to hit your child, you hit him without emotion, just give him a cold-blooded slap. On the other hand, other psychiatrists have argued that you show your anger because at least then the child knows that you're concerned for him, whereas if you just hit him in a cold-blooded manner, he will think that you don't love him. I think there are all sorts of problems here as to what punishment really is.

Now this raises an equally important question. There is no doubt at all that punishment is extremely widespread in our society, or to put it in neutral terms, the laying on of hands on children by parents is extremely widespread. We know so little of the effects of this kind of behaviour by parents on their children, whether it has desirable or undesirable effects, or some mixture of both. Are we to be prevented from investigating one of the most pervasive areas of human behaviour, particularly parent-child interactions? Or should we find out what effects various kinds of punishment have? I don't really see how we can opt out of an area of this kind, simply because we think it might have some undesirable consequences. Supposing we were able to show experimentally that certain kinds of aversive consequences had, as far as we can judge, only beneficial effects, whereas other kinds of aversive consequences may have some beneficial effects, but also some undesirable effects. If we knew this, then we might feel (and this would be what I would call a political, not a psychological, decision) that we were justified in using certain kinds of aversive stimulation in certain situations, but not in others.

One final point. Dr. Lovibond said, and I have a great deal of sympathy with this, that the clinical psychologist, or the behaviour therapist who is a clinical psychologist, is faced with a case that he has to treat, and therefore he has to do the best with what he's got. Of course it's perfectly true in one sense, but in another sense it represents the greatest danger that behaviour therapy has to face at the present time. One of the points I've been making for a long time is that the whole trouble with clinical psychology for fifty years or more has been its tendency to ape clinical psychiatry, to become a second-rate or pseudo-psychiatry. This is partly a matter of status values, since the clinical psychologist feels, I'm sure, that he will not be appreciated by the psychiatrist unless he talks the psychiatrist's language. And the thing that really worries me about behaviour therapy, the only thing that really worries me, is that the clinical psychologist may get himself into exactly the same position that the psychiatrist is in at the present time; that he will feel he has to treat patients who are presenting for treatment because he cannot withhold treatment from them, rather than that he should be in the position of being a basic research worker.

I am not complaining about what the psychiatrist does. He has responsibility for the patient, he has to give some form of treatment, he has to do the best he can with the resources he has. No one can complain about this. But if this happens to the clinical psychologist as well, if he develops the same attitude that this is

147

his primary task, to use what knowledge he has, here and now, the best way he can, then all I can say is that we're going to get nowhere very slowly. I see the roles of the psychiatrist and the psychologist as complementary. The psychiatrist is a person who applies his own special knowledge, which is primarily in a number of areas of somatic treatment, and, if you like, in psychotherapy. The clinical psychologist's role must surely be developed from his own special training, which is, of course, in the body of knowledge which we call psychology. So I see this basic role of the clinical psychologist as that of a research worker. He can be a research worker at the level of Eysenck, who is trying to discover general principles, not interested in individuals. He can be at the kind of level that Dr. McConaghy is working at, where you carry out experiments as carefully controlled as possible, using groups of patients rather than individuals. Or he can be at the level of basic research with the individual patient, hoping that what he does will, incidentally, at the present time, relieve these abnormalities, change behaviour, that this change will follow on these operations. But there is always the goal in mind that what you are doing is advancing basic knowledge, so that future patients can be treated more rationally than at present.

REFERENCES

1. Prokasy, W.F., *ed.* (1965). *Classical conditioning: a symposium.* New York: Appleton-Century-Crofts.